T
Permaculture
Plot

Compiled by
Simon Pratt

Permanent Publications

Published by
Permanent Publications
Hyden House Limited
Little Hyden Lane
Clanfield
Hampshire
PO8 0RU
England
Tel: (01705) 596500
Fax: (01705) 595834
Email: permaculture@gn.apc.org
WWW: http:www.uea.ac.uk/~e415/home.html

© 1996 Simon Pratt

Design by
Tim Harland, Permanent Publications

Typesetting by Simon Pratt

Cover photograph
Graham Bell and Nancy Woodhead's garden in the Scottish Borders
See 'Earthward' entry on page 18 for details of their work
Photo by Tim Harland

Printed by
St. Richard's Press,
Leigh Road, Chichester, West Sussex PO19 2TU

British Library Cataloguing in Publication Data
A catalogue record for this book is available from the British Library

ISBN 1 85623 010 4

Contents

Illustrations

All photographs and illustrations have been supplied from source except those on the following pages which have been supplied, or redrawn from originals, by:

Simon Pratt   27, 37, 51, 63, 115, 123, 133
Chris Hoppe   94, 113
Tim Harland   114
Key overlays to plans by Simon Pratt and Tim Harland

What is Perma-culture?

We can live in a more natural and environmentally friendly way and significantly improve our quality of life.

By thinking carefully about the way we use our resources – food, energy, shelter and other material and non-material needs – it is possible to get much more out of life by using less. We can be more productive for less effort, reaping benefits for our environment and ourselves, for now and for generations to come.

This is the essence of **Permaculture** – the design of an ecologically sound way of living – in our households, gardens, communities and businesses. It is created by cooperating with Nature and caring for the Earth and its people.

The principles and practice of permaculture can be used by anyone, anywhere:

- ❀ City flats, yards and window boxes
- ❀ Suburban and rural houses/gardens
- ❀ Allotments and smallholdings
- ❀ Community spaces
- ❀ Farms and estates
- ❀ Countryside and conservation areas
- ❀ Commercial and industrial premises
- ❀ Educational establishments
- ❀ Waste ground...

Permaculture empowers the individual to be resourceful, self-reliant and a conscious part of the solution to the many problems facing us – both locally and globally.

Preface

Welcome to the fourth edition of *The Permaculture Plot*. I am pleased to present 86 examples of permaculture design principles being put into practice in these islands. If you come across any more worthy of inclusion, please let me know. I have not adopted any selection criteria in compiling this directory, although I have encouraged some people to send in an entry. I have not personally visited all the sites, although many are known to me. Many are in the early stages of development, so do not expect to see wonderful flourishing productive systems. I hope they all indicate a way out of our current dilemmas as an over-consuming society, towards a saner, sensible, sustainable future.

Most entries have been reprinted as the contributors have written them, with minor grammatical changes. In some cases significant editing was necessary in order to fit the page, but the words are still those of the contributors, to whom many thanks are due.

With very few exceptions, visitors are welcome at all the sites listed. Please do read the accompanying notes before setting out on your journey of exploration and read the guidance on the next page about visiting sites.

I have set out the entries in a different way this time, which I hope will be helpful – your comments are welcome. They are now listed in a rough geographical order within each region, but adjusted where necessary so that photographs and illustrations are always facing the text of an entry.

Permaculture is definitely catching on in this country: the last edition of this publication listed 52 sites and projects, of which 47 have repeated or updated their entries this time round. The first edition of *The Permaculture Plot*, published by the Permaculture Association in 1985, listed a mere seven projects! So I look forward to the next edition with at least 120 entries (with your help) – *see page 141 for further details.*

Simon Pratt (Compiler)
June 1996

Editorial Address
Redfield Community Buckingham Road Winslow BUCKINGHAM MK18 3LZ

Telephone
(01296) 712161

Fax
(01296) 714983

E-mail
106031,2416@ compuserve.com
or
pcbritain@ gn.apc.org

Visiting Sites

Many of these sites are not public. Do not under any circumstances visit these without arranging to do so first by phoning or writing. Public sites will usually have an entrance fee, which may vary from time to time. People who do not charge may equally appreciate a gift to thank them for their time and effort, or an equal amount of your time doing a useful job. Please respect the views of someone who says they are not available to see you.

If you visit these sites people may wish to hear your views, or they may simply be willing to show you their work. Do not expect people to want to hear from you 'how they could be doing it better'. They often have a very clear picture of that themselves and are just working through their priorities.

Please respect the privacy and time of people you contact.

Information has been provided to make visiting these sites as straightforward as possible.

BA means you may visit the site by arrangement with the contact person. If there is a note to say there is no accommodation, please make your own arrangements.

WWOOF means you may visit as a member of the national organisation, Working Weekends On Organic Farms. WWOOF is a countrywide exchange network where bed and board and practical experience are given in return for work on organic farms and smallholdings. Midweek, long term and overseas stays are also available. Excellent opportunities for organic training or changing to a rural life. Annual subscription £10 to the Membership Secretary, WWOOF, 19 Bradford Road, Lewes, East Sussex BN7 1RB.

WHATEVER HAPPENED TO...?

In any publication of this nature there will be changes as people move on or direct their energies elsewhere. Just for the record, I am including brief notes on those entries which appeared in the last edition (January 1994), but which do not appear this time round. It is remarkable that it is only five of those 52 entries. Seven changes are listed below, but two of these have moved to new sites described in this edition.

Duartbeg: Emma and Bernard Planterose have moved down the road into the 80 acre Leckmelm Wood (*see page 11*). The current occupants of Duartbeg were invited to contribute to this edition but have not responded.

Windermere: Debbie Binch no longer feels there is enough to show in her garden to justify being included this time.

Solihull: Laura Englefield has decided that an entry is no longer appropriate.

Higham Marsh: John van der Post and Maryjane Preece have moved on. Last reports were that John was importing rickshaws from India to Greece!

Rosehill: Peter Ratcliff has left his parents' home in Hertfordshire and is now based at Keveral Farm in Cornwall (*see page 129*).

Agroforestry Research Trust: The trial mixed fruiting woodland plot in North Devon continues, but Martin Crawford has decided to describe his new site, the Schumacher Forest Garden in South Devon this time (*see page 121*).

Bath: Helen Woodley is currently studying in Sheffield and her allotments are being caretaken on a minimal maintenance/fertility building basis.

Helen is one of a select group who featured in the first edition of *The Permaculture Plot* back in 1986. Three of the people and places are also included in this edition: Rod Everett at Middle Wood, Pen Strange at Tyn-y-Fron and Arthur Hollins at Fordhall Farm.

INDEX TO PERMACULTURE SITES

Site Name	Page	Size	Date	Region
Leckmelm Wood	11	81.5	1993	Scotland
Little Ash	124	80	1983	S & SW England
Lower Rowley Cottage	128	0.5	1976	S & SW England
Lower Shaw Farm	112	3.2	1974	S & SW England
Maen Offeiriad	44	5	1995	Wales/Borders
Manor Heath	28	<1	1992	North England
Middle Wood	21	235	1984	North England
Monkey Sanctuary	130	12	1992	S & SW England
Mossburnford Mill	19	2	1983	Scotland
Nature's World	24	26	1994	North England
Naturewise	84	0.2	1991	E & SE England
New Barn Field Centre	120	20	1989	S & SW England
Pen-y-Bryn	36	4.5	1993	Wales/Borders
Plants For A Future	132	28	1990	S & SW England
Prickly Nut Wood	110	8	1992	S & SW England
Primrose Farm	52	6	1988	Wales/Borders
Ragmans Lane	58	60	1990	Wales/Borders
Redfield	80	17	1978	E & SE England
Redruth	135	1	1992	S & SW England
Reigate	98	3.5	1984	E & SE England
Riverside Comm. Garden	54	0.01	1995	Wales/Borders
Rose Garth	60	5.5	1989	Wales/Borders
Rubha Phoil	12	15	1990	Scotland
Ryton Forest Garden	71	0.25	1993	Middle England
Schumacher Forest Garden	121	2.1	1994	S & SW England
Shrub Family	75	1	1991	E & SE England
South Molton	122	0.016	1991	S & SW England
Springfield Comm. Garden	30	7.5	1993	North England
Springhill	82	186	1990	E & SE England
Tai Madog	35	3	1988	Wales/Borders
Tir Penrhos Isaf	40	7.2	1985	Wales/Borders
Todmorden	26	0.5	1990	North England
Tottenham Green	86	0.01	1994	E & SE England
Troutwells	126	2	1992	S & SW England
Turners Field	118	3.6	1986	S & SW England
Tyn-y-Fron	38	6	1983	Wales/Borders
Unicorn Cottage	117	0.5	1985	S & SW England
Wadebridge	134	7.5	1993	S & SW England
Wells	116	1.8	1983	S & SW England
Wenhaston	76	0.5	1995	E & SE England
West Wood	73	200	1990	Middle England
Westcliff-on-Sea	92	0.1	1994	E & SE England
Woking	96	0.1	1993	E & SE England
Y Felin	42	7	1992	Wales/Borders

Scotland

1 Leckmelm Wood, Ullapool
2 Rubha Phoil, Skye
3 Corrary, Loch Alsh
4 Fortingall, Aberfeldy
5 Auchinleck, Ayrshire
6 Earthward, Melrose
7 Mossburnford Mill, Jedburgh

L eckmelm Wood is a 35 year old ex-Forestry Commission plantation 2 miles from Ullapool, on the south facing slopes above Loch Broom. On deep mineral soils, with burns, gullies and cliffs, it is being transformed into a diverse, multi-purpose, multi-species, inhabited forest garden.

The Planterose family are inhabitants, under the canopy and in their self-built, one-room, wholly organic, pole-frame cabin. Ponds, clearings and paths have been excavated, providing spoil and space for planting useful, mainly edible, perennials. Fruiting bushes edge the tracks and a large polytunnel extends growing and living space. Tree nursery, spring water, compost loo, photovoltaic panels, stable and sawmill sheds, huts, gypsy caravan, 3 home-schooled children, 9 chickens, 2 ponies and a mouse-eating pine marten scaring dog are integral to this forest set-up.

We do nearly all the work ourselves, using safe, modern equipment, with occasional help from neighbours, friends and family. Trees are felled selectively or in small coupes, releasing the existing species to grow on and allowing space and light enough to establish other hardwoods, orchards and meadows. Timber is extracted using the ponies and small-scale machinery and milled on our portable chainsaw mill or at the local sawmill. Scots pine, Douglas fir and Sitka spruce, it is used mainly for wooden buildings built by our tree business 'North Woods'. Thinnings are sold or bartered locally as firewood and the forest also yields wild berries, nuts, venison and edible fungi. Dense, rampant rhododendron is one liability we are trying hard to turn into an asset – makes good charcoal, turning wood and amuses energetic children.

At present communications are through the office in Martin Howard's home nearby, which is also a nerve centre for the renowned 'Reforesting Scotland'. One day we might hang a telephone on a tree outside the cabin. Maybe.

SCOTLAND

1

Leckmelm Wood

Address
c/o The Old Mill House
ULLAPOOL
Wester Ross
IV26 2TB

Telephone
(01854) 612509
messages

Fax/E-mail
(01854) 612900

Contact
Emma & Bernard Planterose

Date est.
1993

Size/acres
81.5

Residents
5

Visitors
BA

2

Rubha Phoil

Address
Rubha Phoil
Armadail Pier
Ardvasar
Sleat
ISLE OF SKYE
IV45 8RS

Telephone
(01471) 844312
messages

Fax/E-mail

Contact
Sandra Masson,
David Wilkinson

Date est.
1990

Size/acres
15

Residents
3

Visitors
BA

Rubha Phoil is a 15 acre wooded peninsula situated beside the busy Armadale (to Mallaig) ferry terminal. An untouched wilderness for 50 years and an inaccessibility to sheep has resulted in massive natural regeneration of trees. I am growing and selling herbs and because of our unique site and close proximity to the ferry we are being encouraged by our local planning officer to become a Centre of Alternative Technology – Input / ideas please! People wishing to be P.A.L.S. (Permaculture Alternative Living Systems) of the Rubha please contact us!

This year my composting, shredding and associated beneficial plants demonstration area will have to be improved (tidied even?) as will the worm farms. Last year's students were a great help and the Forest Garden now boasts more herbs, the Peace Garden, steps and a willow arbour. This was originally planted with the help of local Baha'i's – a good source of enthusiastic labour!

Our multi-purpose workshop is now more or less complete and this year we have added an eco bath-house with compost toilets. A wooden bothy was also built from recycled materials. Water is collected from all roofs and power from wind generators.

Sam's home-made shredder still works well and his wind-powered models bring enjoyment to both residents and visitors alike! The woodland walk also attracts visitors of many nationalities and this could be expanded to include structures inspired by the Institute of Earth Education (as we were inspired).

A local crofter is helping us rebuild sea-retaining stone walls which surround a fertile area of a number of acres. This land would be ideal to set up as an example of sustainable Community Supported Agriculture: lots of seaweed close by and a growing number of Skyelanders asking for organic food. We have a thriving LETS, a beautifully illustrated local magazine, a changing culture and a gently-emerging Agenda 21 makes Skye an exciting place to be! We have summer accommodation for 'diggers and altruists'!

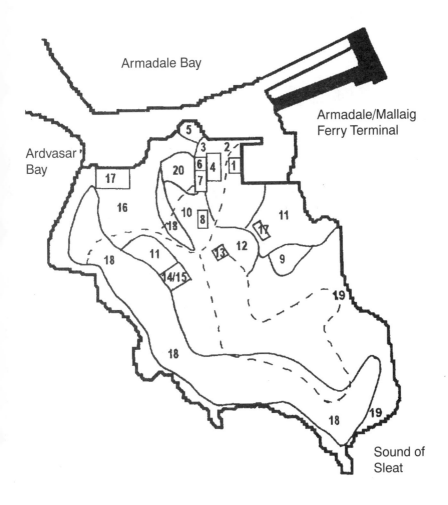

Rubha Phoil

Armadale Bay

Armadale/Mallaig
Ferry Terminal

Ardvasar
Bay

Sound of
Sleat

1   Planned retail facility
2   Braille herb garden walk
3   Herb garden nursery
4   Polytunnel (unique wooden design)
5   Ponds with appropriate wetland
     planting of edible/useful species
6   Compost toilets
7   General purpose workshop and
     storage shelter
8   Herb garden and composting area
9   Agroforestry. Interplanting with soft/top
     ruit, vegetables and herbs
10   Large open area

11   Private accommodation, with Zone 1
     organic vegetable and herb garden
     and Zone 2/3 fruit plantings
12   Forest Garden
13   Start of Woodland Nature Trail
14   Planned wet weather/student
     seminar facility
15   Planned permaculture course venue
     and accommodation
16   Wild flower meadow
17   Tree nurseries
18   Shelter belt
19   Viewing points
20   Orchard

3

Corrary

Address
Corrary
Glen Beag
Glenelg
KYLE OF
LOCHALSH
Wester Ross
IV40 8JX

Telephone
(01599) 522258

Fax/E-mail
(01599) 522288

Contact
Neil & Maggie
Sutherland

Date est.
1992

Size/acres
725

Residents
4

Visitors
BA

Corrary Farm is situated on the West coast Highlands a couple of miles from the coast and opposite the southern part of the Isle of Skye. A partnership purchased the land in the summer of 1992. The land extends to some 725 acres of typically Highland hill and glen, denuded by livestock over the past 250 or so years. Our plans include for helping the land change from its presently impoverished state to that of abundance ecologically, socially and every other life giving way. We are therefore involved in the following areas of activity:

- *Reforestation:* Establishing some 400 acres of multi-type woodland; wildwoods, managed conifer and deciduous planting, energy woods, orchards, coppice etc.

- *Ecological building:* Developing a suitable range of building types for local conditions, using locally sourced materials particularly timber.

- *Horticulture/Tree nursery:* Involvement in the local food economy with the production of high quality organic produce. Locally sourced tree planting as a backdrop to more complex mixtures of plants specific by design.

- *Animals:* We currently run a flock of 60 breeding ewes on the fenced inbye. We also integrate pigs and domestic fowl in our land-use.

- *Child-rearing:* Two pre-school people and plenty of room for more.

We are investigating ways of returning Corrary to the peopled place of former years with the subdivision of croftland subject to personal need and long term community stability. As for accommodation, we have a very basic residential caravan available to anyone serious enough to help and assist in our day to day work and objectives.

W hen we bought the old school house in Fortingall we were facing a huge undertaking: transform the old school into a warm and welcoming home from inside and out and make something special from the garden. The plot is just under an acre. Those who know me from the time that I lived in Garth Castle as Maryse Vogelaar, know that I had my hands full running the castle as an Open House. My experience in gardening was nil. So after reading numerous books on gardening I started digging six foot deep trenches to clear them from all the nasty weeds you can imagine, line them with plastic to prevent the weeds from creeping in again and started working my way through the mountain of dug out soil to sift out the tiny roots. That was July 1994. In April 1995 I was facing a back garden still three-quarters filled with that mountain.

Then I read about permaculture, which teaches us that we have to learn to put in the minimum energy for the maximum output. I followed the advice given in the books on permaculture and started to make raised beds: I spread the pile of weeded soil on the garden; lined it with a thick layer of cardboard, well overlapped; made timber frames and filled them with a layer of organic waste, then a 15cm layer of rotted horse manure and another 15cm layer of spent hops, which I collected from the local brewery. Then I made pockets in the hops, filled them with (good) soil and planted my seedlings (which I had raised in individual tiny pots made out of newspaper). The pots will decompose and the roots grow through the paper.

WITHIN THREE MONTHS the garden provided us with all the vegetables we need; everything grows in abundance without any show of pests; we only watered it once even though we had that long spell of heat and drought. The only plants we watered regularly were the seedlings in the coldframes.

People started coming from afar to have a look at it: even a lady from Australia, who is a friend of Bill Mollison came, as she had heard of this 'miracle'. She called it a miracle, but this is the way permaculture gardens do look, all the books on permaculture promise us. They prove to be right!

SCOTLAND

4

Fortingall

Address
Culdees
Fortingall
ABERFELDY
Perthshire
PH15 2NF

Telephone
(01887) 830519

Fax/E-mail

Contact
Maryse Anand-Vervaik

Date est.
1994

Size/acres
1

Residents
2

Visitors
BA, WWOOF

5

Auchinleck

Address
Butterworths'
Organic Nursery
Garden Cottage
Auchinleck
Estate
CUMNOCK
Ayrshire
KA18 2LR

Telephone
(01290) 551088

Fax/E-mail

Contact
John & Donna
Butterworth

Date est.
1985

Size/acres
2

Residents
5

Visitors
BA, WWOOF

Our small nursery is set amongst 300 acres of broadleaved woodland on the banks of the River Lugar, 10 miles inland from Ayr. We are 300 feet above sea level and somewhat frost-prone. We are the first commercial organic raisers of fruit trees in Britain. We are keen to encourage the enormous hidden potential for fruit tree growing in Western Scotland. In the process we will be contributing towards the essential decentralisation of the economy. However, we are happy to supply trees to anyone for whom the 'organic' aspect overrides the 'local', or who is unable to source certain varieties locally.

Also on the commercial front, we raise crops for Ayrshire Organic Growers, an annual subscription box scheme and of which we were founder members. These crops include transplants of various kinds raised in a lean-to solar greenhouse.

The latter is the link between 'commercial' and 'domestic' in that it is not only used for raising transplants, but also acts as passive solar heating for the dwelling (it extends along the entire south side). We calculate that it has reduced the need for fuel by 2 months in the year for house heating. The greenhouse contains a number of 200 litre water drums for heat storage.

Domestically, the dwelling, though very old, has been fitted with four inches of insulation in the walls and eight inches in the roof. Rainwater collection is in progress from another 30 x 34 foot wooden greenhouse.

We have a small forest garden and a number of raised beds, producing most of our own fruit and veg. We also have hens, bees and an impending house cow. We make use of various structures – walls, sheds and caravan for training fruit and we are establishing a collection of apples (about 50 to date). We are fortunate to live adjacent to some 300 acres of ancient broadleaved woodland which we use for firewood, small constructions etc..

*The solar greenhouse at John and Donna Butterworth's
Organic Nursery on the Auchinleck Estate.*

6

Earthward

Address
Earthward
Tweed Horizons
Newtown St
Boswells
Roxburghshire
TD6 0SG

Telephone
(01835) 822122

Fax/E-mail
(01835) 822199
earthwrd@
scotborders.co.uk

Contact
Graham Bell

Date est.
1994

Size/acres
10

Residents
None

Visitors
BA, no accommodation

The site nestles in a bend in the River Tweed and has a southward aspect over the beautiful Borders countryside. Originally a monastery built in the 1930s it is now a local enterprise centre for sustainable development.

There are several demonstrations in the grounds:
- A young forest garden including a gene bank of useful top fruit and nut cultivars.
- A restored orchard and organic fruit and vegetable garden.
- An agroforestry trial with strip planting of native woodlands amidst pasture on a steep hillside.

We are building a gene bank of rare and hard to obtain biological material especially adapted to our regional climate. Biodiversity is an important key to sustainability. We are pioneering pest and disease control through building natural prevention. Courses are run and work experience placements are available. We have an extensive library and are developing added value products with emphasis on rural regeneration, particularly for depopulated areas like our own. We specialise in north hardy varieties and low work high output techniques.

We offer a programme which includes:
- Education through publications and courses.
- Skills training through work placements.
- Landscape design and contracting.
- Ideas for land use diversification.
- Employment initiatives.
- Community regeneration exercises.
- Resource assessment.
- Business plan preparation.
- Meetings and action plan facilitation.
- Invigoration of small businesses.
- Innovation evaluation.

Our work often appears 'low tech'. We use front edge technology wherever it is appropriate, from the Internet to the latest machine tools. In biological systems our techniques are often transparent; it may be the thinking behind the design which is the advanced element!

We have two acres; a narrow strip of land about a quarter of a mile long with the river Jed Water forming the Southern boundary and a 50 foot high cliff to the North. There are two houses and workshops one of which used to be a water driven sawmill.

The area we chose for vegetables had been poor pasture. We had this ploughed in the first year and laid out as deep beds cropped on a multiple four course rotation. Between crops the beds are covered with black polythene and the system is easy to operate and productive. A lot of compost is made from grass cuttings etc..

We planted a wide selection of soft fruit which, from past experience, we knew was the most productive thing in the garden with least effort. We also planted tree fruit. We eat our own fruit, fresh, frozen or in jam all the year.

I have kept bees for a long time and now have a productive apiary – seven hives at present.

We have solar panels for hot water and burn wood in a stove that heats water and supplies radiators. Both houses are well insulated.

We have planted alder and willow for coppicing for firewood. We have also planted oak, ash, beech and decorative species. There have been few failures and growth is good.

We have sought to improve the environment for birds and animals. In addition to the planted trees we have left many areas wild; already there are orchids appearing spontaneously. All this has led to a increase in birds – I have identified over 50 bird species most of which are here regularly. We have a colony of pipistrelle bats in the roof and hedgehogs, moles, mice, frogs and toads are often seen.

7

Mossburnford Mill

Address
Mossburnford Mill
JEDBURGH
Roxburghshire
TD8 6PJ

Telephone
(01835) 840344

Fax/E-mail

Contact
David & Marina Catt

Date est.
1983

Size/acres
2

Residents
6

Visitors
BA

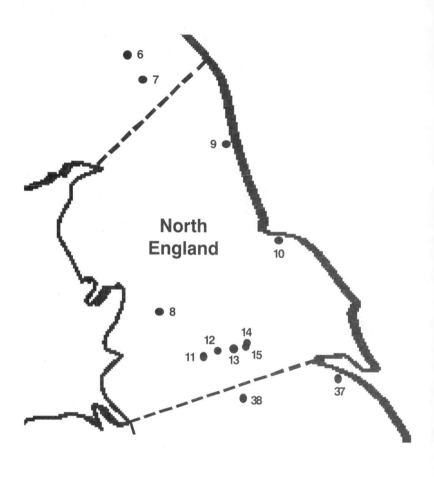

North
England

8 Middle Wood, Lancaster
9 Drift Permaculture, Newcastle
10 Nature's World, Middlesbrough
11 Carr House Fold, Todmorden
12 Wicken Hill Farm, Hebden Bridge
13 Manor Heath, Halifax
14 Springfield, Bradford
15 Bradford City Farm

8

Middle Wood

Middle Wood Charitable Trust runs a small study centre which experiments with sheep's wool insulation and passive solar heat gain. It has a turf roof and is powered by a Proven wind generator. This building is used for running a variety of Green/Permaculture courses and sleeps 10 people in bunk beds. It is located in a beautiful wooded valley which appears to have an overlying important earth energy based on ancient sacred orchards. There are many different energy lines going through it and a spiral centred on an old holly and a spiral of hawthorns. We are just beginning to get a feel for what this means as we find many friends, healers and green aware people on these lines.

At the current time we are rebuilding the demonstration organic garden incorporating lots of pattern and have many other plans ready for action if funds come in. These include Internet based environmental information linked to Europe, a straw bale building for offices, a six month sustainable development course, woodland management trail and woodcraft workshops. At present we have resident Yurt maker.

Middle Wood has been given recognition in Lancashire as one of nine Centres of Environmental Excellence which will help to promote Lancashire's Environmental Action Programme. Middle Wood is the Centre for Raising Awareness in Sustainability. Through this we link closely with the main environmental movement within Lancashire and get a chance to help people move towards a realistic agenda for the 21st Century where we Care for the Earth, Care for People and Care for the Future.

We work with volunteers but hope that in the near future we will get help with funding four part-time employees. At present this is frustrated by a complex government and local politics that we don't understand. Maybe we would be better forgetting all about outside funds? Time will tell.

Local LETSystems in Kendal and Lancaster link up with Middle Wood and through co-operation help to build a stable alternative economy. Please send SAE for newsletter and latest events list.

Address
Middle Wood
Roeburndale
West
Wray
LANCASTER
LA2 8QX

Telephone
(015242) 21880

Fax/E-mail
Middlewood@
lancaster.ac.uk

Contact
Rod Everett

Date est.
1984

Size/acres
235

Residents
3-5

Visitors
BA, working
volunteers

9

Drift

Address
*Drift Permaculture Project
John Marley
Centre
Muscott Grove
Whickham View
Scotswood
NEWCASTLE-
UPON-TYNE
NE15 6TT*

Telephone
*(0191) 200 4726/
4735*

Fax/E-mail

Contact
Ed Tyler

Date est.
1995

Size/acres
1

Residents
None

Visitors
WWOOF

The Drift Permaculture Project is a partnership between the local community, community garden centre, City Challenge, a further education college, the local authority, various local schools, a building/training company and the Permaculture Association (Britain).

It is focused on an acre of land in Scotswood in Newcastle's West End which is being developed as a community garden with the aim of being accessible to all, especially those with special needs. The path network is sunken, with gentle gradients and an all-weather surface, providing plenty of chair-height gardening space for wheelchair users and those gardeners who can't or don't like to bend down. The garden has been designed permaculturally and the designer is working on-site helping get the various partners to implement it. The forest garden has been planted up with top fruit and some soft fruit and the land is being prepared with green manures. A wildlife/fruiting hedge and pond system (using water captured from a nearby roof) are being developed. It is hoped that by the time this is in print there will be a beehive in the courtyard of the adjacent education/training centre and demonstrations/courses run by the local beekeeping association will have begun. Local artists are hoping to make sculptures out of the sandstone 'quarried' when the paths were dug out.

The project has a wider brief: to build gardening skills back into the West End of Newcastle, an area of great social disadvantage with high crime rates. This ambitious aim is dependent upon the securing of further funding (we apply when we get the time!) but in the meantime we have won a couple of national awards: a BT/WWF Partnership Award and Barclays/Age Resource Award. This has enabled us to do some of the skill-building work: for example we have moved a donated greenhouse onto a nearby allotment site where the secretary invites local school children along to raise seedlings (and see his chickens!). We have also helped set up a gardening course for Asian women. The management committee who manages the project is full of ideas about how more this kind of work could be done.

Local schoolchildren help establish the Community Garden at the Drift Permaculture Project. Above: mulching, Below: making compost.

10

Nature's World

Address
Nature's World
The Botanic
Centre
Ladgate Lane
Acklam
MIDDLES-
BROUGH
TS5 7YN

Telephone
(01642) 594895

Fax/E-mail
(01642) 591224

Contact
Anne Press

Date est.
1994

Size/acres
26

Residents
None

Visitors
11-6 daily May-
Oct; 11-4 Wed-
Sun Nov-Apr

The Botanic Centre is a charitable company, set up in 1989 to develop Britain's most exciting and innovative environmental demonstration centre. Nature's World at the Botanic Centre aims to show the public and school children how industry, local government, the education authorities and the local community can work together to improve quality of life and the environment.

The Botanic Centre market garden has been producing organic vegetables for the last five years. One full time gardener and a number of horticultural trainees look after the cropping on a day to day basis and are helped regularly by enthusiastic volunteers. Producing food for local sale with the help of local people has increasingly seen the market gardens become a focus for local community involvement. The market garden covers approximately four acres and includes both field crops and protected cropping. The subscription scheme has been designed to provide 7lbs of produce weekly to scheme members and aims to provide a weekly collection of vegetables 52 weeks a year.

Part of the organic market garden is being developed as a forest garden. Our aim is for the main area of the forest garden to be planted with fruiting trees and shrubs of various heights. Fruit trees are expensive. Initially we are buying four standard fruit trees for the upper fruiting layer and we have rescued twelve fruit trees of unknown type from the plant sales area. These, together with others that we will graft from the numerous varieties already at Nature's World, will form the framework of our forest garden. We hope eventually that members of the public will adopt our fruit trees.

The permaculture tyre garden at Nature's World was started in March 1994 by reusing old tyres, courtesy of North Eastern Tyres. This reduced wasteful landfilling and created a range of habitats in which to sustain a multifunctional food bearing garden containing herbs, vegetables and fruit. The community was involved as most plants and seeds were salvaged from our visitor gardens or from other nurseries, nothing is refused, everything has its use. Gardeners included children and mentally and physically handicapped people. Seed has been collected for future use.

Spring 1994
Building tyre
garden. Large
tyre to become
pond.

Late May 1994
Elephant face
(back left)
marks pond,
with water
coming out
of trunk.

July 1994
Children help
in the garden.
Some plants:
− comfrey
− peas
− chamomile
− marigold
− spinach
− phacelia

11

Todmorden

Address
7 Carr House Fold
TODMORDEN
Lancashire
OL14 8AR

Telephone
(01706) 818902

Fax/E-mail

Contact
Pam Colbran

Date est.
1990

Size/acres
0.5

Residents
2

Visitors
BA

The garden rises steeply behind the house and is terraced. The terracing helps prevent run-off water loss, provides easier mobility around the garden and creates lots of edge potential. Three ponds now add to the diversity and help to create more of a balance in the overall garden system. Unfortunately, the spring that fed the ponds has dried up so plants are relied on to oxygenate the water. The slug population is visibly reduced with the influx of frogs and some goldfish provide predators for the abundant mosquito larvae.

The different levels, the two greenhouses and the variety of microclimates created by establishing hedging allow a range of fruit, vegetable and salad crops to produce themselves. The lower levels tend to be regularly visited crops, the compost heap and greenhouses. The upper levels being mainly fruit crops including the forest garden, a rockery area and sitting areas to admire the view. The majority of the plants are perennial supplying some of the household's food, medicinal (about which I am still learning) and craft work needs.

Rainwater harvesting is working well on one of the greenhouses but a better system is under review for the other. The next big projects are effective rainwater harvesting from the house with large storage tanks and a compost loo.

The garden really stood up to its permaculture test when we left it for 10 months whilst travelling abroad. Neighbours and friends were told to harvest any food and one trusted friend was allowed to prune a little. Otherwise the garden was left to itself. It only required three days of tending to return it to its normal state of being loved.

T his smallholding of 6.5 acres lies at 1050 feet, overlooking the Calder Valley, with a South facing aspect. The family of four adults and two children have lived here for nine years. The land is gradually being transformed from sheep and dairy grazing to trees and perennial crops. Projects so far set up include a shelterbelt of indigenous trees, a paddock for wildlife, watercress in streams, mushrooms on logs, raised beds on a deep-mulch, no-dig system, perennial herbs, vegetables and flowers, water barrels and butts, comfrey and nettle jauches, chicken and geese keeping, microclimate creation for young and tender crops.

Recent projects include investigation into biodynamic gardening methods, creation of biodynamic compost heap and spraying for nutrition and root crops. Future projects include beekeeping and more efficient water recycling. The main necessity however is more efficient use of energy/heat for the farmhouse. We are looking into three possibilities – small wind generator, solar panels and anaerobic digestion, maybe all three if finances allow – any suggestions would be gladly received.

12

Hebden Bridge

Address
Wicken Hill Farm
Heights Road
HEBDEN
BRIDGE
West Yorkshire
HX7 5RF

Telephone
(01422) 885249

Fax/E-mail

Contact
Marilyn Edwards

Date est.
1990

Size/acres
6.5

Residents
6

Visitors
BA

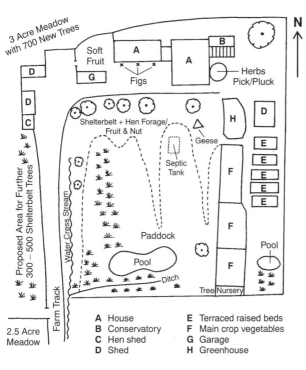

A	House	E	Terraced raised beds
B	Conservatory	F	Main crop vegetables
C	Hen shed	G	Garage
D	Shed	H	Greenhouse

13

Manor Heath

Address
*Manor Heath
Demonstration
Gardens
Manor Heath
Road
HALIFAX
West Yorkshire
HX3*

Telephone
(01274) 584089

Fax/E-mail

Contact
Mark Fisher

Date est.
1992

Size/acres
<1

Residents
None

Visitors
*10-4 daily Apr-
Sep; Sat & Sun
Oct-Mar*

An ornamental kitchen garden and a forest garden were built by Calder Valley Organic Gardeners in the winter of 1992/93. These two gardens – now fully productive – were additions to their existing demonstration areas inside a large walled garden operated by Calderdale Council. Both gardens are small and self-contained to reflect local garden sizes. The walled garden is open every day.

The ornamental kitchen garden is a mix of styles from cottage gardening to permaculture. The aim of the garden is to be productive while at the same time delighting with seasonal blossoms, scents and colours. Mixed together are perennials, shrubs and climbers interplanted with vegetables. The informality of the planting attracts beneficial predator insects into the garden, so creating a natural balance. Keyhole beds for a three course rotation, a herb spiral, mulch basket for raspberries and an attractive cuttable mulch bed, are features taken from permaculture. A wildlife pond, rockery, bench seat, compost bin and leafmould heap represent the more orthodox.

The forest garden is loosely based on the practice of Robert Hart, the design achieving economy of space and labour. The emphasis is on perennial food crops grown in spatial association related to their height and spread – the storeys or layers in a forest are the analogy. The taller fruiting trees form the canopy or upper storey, with the shrub fruit and layers of perennials forming the middle and lower storeys. The design takes direction of sunlight into consideration as required in temperate conditions.

The forest garden is well served with paths and the growing areas are permanently mulched. Along with traditional tree and shrub foods, the less common fruits have been planted, these often being in ornamental use in gardens. Self seeding annual leaf crops compliment the perennial vegetables, leaves and herbs.

Manor Heath
Ornamental Kitchen Garden

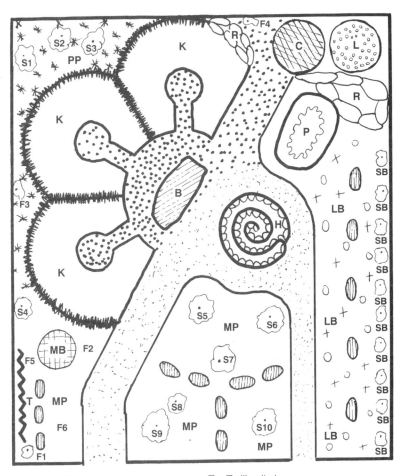

C Compost bin
H Herb spiral
K Keyhole bed
L Leafmold stack
LB Legume/borage cuttable mulch border
MB Mulch basket
MP Mixed planting:
  vegetables, annuals, perennials
P Pond
PP Perennial plants (ornamental)
R Rockery

T Trellis climbers
F **Fruit**
  1-blackcurrant 2-raspberries
  3-apple (espalier) 4-loganberry
  5-blackberry 6-strawberries
S **Shrubs**
  1-buddleia 2-lavatera 3-willow
  4-winter jasmine 5-mahonia
  6-skimmia 7-viburnum 8-artemisia
  9-mahonia 10-philadelphus
SB Shrub - broom

 Woodchip path   Stone and shingle path   Stepping stone

 Shrub   Bed edging (chives or stones)

14

Springfield Community Garden

Address
Stirling Crescent
Holmewood
BRADFORD
BD4

Telephone
(01274) 753924

Fax/E-mail

Contact
Chris Mackenzie
Davey

Date est.
1993

Size/acres
7.5

Residents
None

Visitors
BA, no accom-
modation

Springfield Community Garden is within the Holmewood Housing Estate in South East Bradford and is a component of the five year programme of improvements to the area. The design has been developed from a brief put together by local people. It includes the following main components:

- The growing of food stuffs, vegetables, fish, poultry and eggs, nuts and berries etc. for local use. Specialised growing of high value cash crops such as garlic, coriander, land and water cress and winter salads is intended.

- Provision of training opportunities for people with learning difficulties.

- Garden design and maintenance education for local people.

- Provision of plants and materials related to edible landscaping to local gardeners.

- Food processing and home economics facilities.

- Open space area to provide recreation and playing space within sight of the kitchen for young people accompanying adults onto the site.

- Provision of workshop spaces for carpentry and green woodwork activities.

The permaculture design seeks to create an abundant and delightful landscape which encourages an air of active sociability around self reliance and healthy eating. The produce will make significant differences to the household economies of participating gardeners and will encourage people to take charge of developing proactive and practical strategies for the relief of poverty.

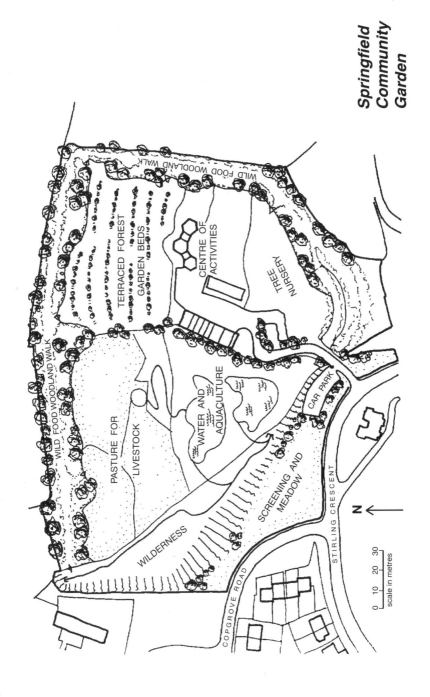

Springfield Community Garden

WILD FOOD WOODLAND WALK

TERRACED FOREST

GARDEN BEDS

CENTRE OF ACTIVITIES

TREE NURSERY

WILD FOOD WOODLAND WALK

PASTURE FOR LIVESTOCK

WATER AND AQUACULTURE

CAR PARK

WILDERNESS

SCREENING AND MEADOW

STIRLING CRESCENT

COPGROVE ROAD

N

0 10 20 30
scale in metres

15

Bradford City Farm

Address
Bradford City Farm
Illingworth Fields
Walker Drive
BRADFORD
West Yorkshire
BD8 9ES

Telephone
(01274) 543500

Fax/E-mail

Contact
Louise Willis,
Gerry McIntyre

Date est.
1983

Size/acres
4

Residents
None

Visitors
Anytime, not Fri

B radford City Farm is sited on a hillside over-looking the city centre and is surrounded by housing estates and industrial areas. The farm is home to a wide variety of animals whose primary use is to bring pleasure to and educate the local children. In true permaculture style however, they do have more than one function – producing eggs for sale, manure for mulching and to cultivate the land.

Until recently this aspect of the farm was predominant, that is until a number of 72 hour permaculture design course students got involved! The garden areas have now begun development, using a mixture of keyhole and raised beds, herb spirals and a small forest garden. The beds will be mulched with manure and black polythene until planting and a no-dig organic system will be used. The type of produce grown will include cash crops, animal feed, flowers, herbs and unusual vegetables.

Many areas of the farm are left as protected wildlife pockets, including a well established pond with an abundance of frogs and dragonflies. Work is currently taking place to link these pockets using a woodland walk. This will incorporate a meadow and marsh area.

The buildings of the farm provide shelter and storage space and improvements, including a roof garden and vertical growing, need to be made to increase its functional capacity and aesthetic appearance. The farm is run by a   ›er of staff and several   ers. Your help is alw   ›lcome.

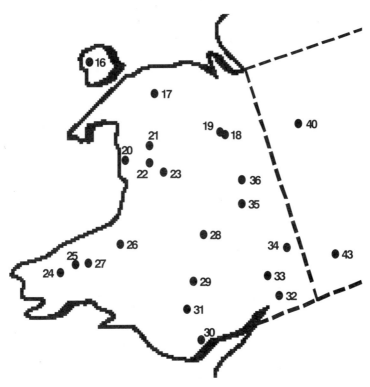

16 Bodedern, Anglesey
17 Tai Madog, Caernarfon
18 Pen-y-Bryn, Oswestry
19 Tyn-y-Fron, Oswestry
20 Chicken Shack, Tywyn
21 Tir Penrhos, Dolgellau
22 Centre for Alternative Technology, Machynlleth
23 Y Felin, Machynlleth
24 Maen Offeiriad, Cardigan
25 Erw Deg, Newcastle Emlyn
26 Gelli Ddewi Isaf, Lampeter
27 Dyfed Permaculture Farm Trust, Newcastle Emlyn
28 Colva, Newchurch, Kington
29 Primrose Farm, Brecon
30 Riverside Community Garden, Cardiff
31 Blaennantygroes Farm, Aberdare
32 Camphill Water, Gloucester
33 Ragman's Lane Farm, Ross-on-Wye
34 Rose Garth, Malvern
35 Earthworm, Ludlow
36 Highwood Hill, Church Stretton

16

Bodedern

Address
Pen Llywenan
Bodedern
HOLYHEAD
Anglesey
LL65 4TS

Telephone
(01407) 740767

Fax/E-mail

Contact
Patricia Knox

Date est.
1994

Size/acres
0.75

Residents
2

Visitors
BA

This three-quarter acre garden was created from the corner of a ten acre windswept field about 15 years ago. Over the years a substantial windbreak had been created and there are also a number of mature fruit trees and bushes.

During the first year in which a permaculture design was applied to the garden, more windbreak species were planted, together with nut trees and some new exotic plants. Many herbs were introduced and a wildflower area has replaced some of the previously mown grass. It is intended that much of the grass area at present needing cutting should be replaced by shrubs, trees and herbs in the future, gradually reducing the need for grass-cutting machines.

Raised beds and terraced areas have been created to grow this year's vegetables. A pergola has also been constructed and it is intended that the climbing plants will add to the windbreak.

Solar collectors from reclaimed domestic radiators give the household hot water system a welcome boost and the conservatory also adds to household solar gain.

In the field beyond the garden, three acres of trees have been planted. As they grow and create more shelter, more of the field, at present grazed by sheep, may be incorporated into the design.

Future plans include a pond and swale system, to make use of roof water and grey water and the introduction of hens.

We live in a terraced house and have been developing the land on the hillside directly behind us along permaculture principles. The land is rocky and poor having formerly been rough grazing for sheep and horses. On the relatively flat ground nearest the house we have an area of approximately 25 raised beds where we grow a wide selection of vegetables organically using lots of mulches, which is sufficient to feed ourselves for most of the year. We are particularly interested in growing unusual food crops – both annual and perennial, as a means of diversification. We also have a polytunnel where we grow a number of less hardy crops such as peppers and tomatoes along with perennials such as kiwi fruit and grape vines. We use several of the raised beds for the production of seeds and tubers of unusual vegetables and fruits.

The propagation of plants takes place in 'The Pit', a dry-stone walled, polythene clad small greenhouse dug into the ground in an attempt to maintain a more even temperature. In association with the raised bed area are shelterbelts of native tree species and several ponds. We have planted two areas of orchards/forest gardens where we have a variety of common and unusual fruit and nut trees, along with fruit bushes, herbs, perennial vegetables and clovers. We have four hives of bees in the lower orchard adjacent to an area of semi-mature oak trees.

Next to the upper orchard are several terraced beds for fruit and vegetable growing and several plots where we are attempting to grow grains using no-till Fukuoka type methods. The highest part of the land, furthest from the house has been planted up with over 1000 native trees – hopefully giving us a wood supply in the long term as well as helping to reforest an area much subject to the overgrazing of sheep.

WALES/ BORDERS

17

Tai Madog

Address
3 Tai Madog
Stablau
Llanrug
CAERNARFON
Gwynedd
LL55 3PH

Telephone
(01758) 750368

Fax/E-mail

Contact
Jill Jackson

Date est.
1988

Size/acres
3

Residents
2

Visitors
BA

18

Pen-y-Bryn

Address
*Pen-y-Bryn Hall
Waterfalls Road
Llanrhaeadr-ym-
Mochnant
OSWESTRY
Shropshire
SY10 0BY*

Telephone
(01691) 780672

Fax/E-mail

Contact
*Lesley Sweet,
Ian Garland*

Date est.
1993

Size/acres
4.5

Residents
2

Visitors
BA

We moved from London to Wales two years ago with grand ideas of what we were going to do: huge veg garden; planting broadleaf, willow, fruit trees; a few livestock – chickens, ducks, goat, bees – not so fast! We also have a house to build.

We have 4.5 acres on a south facing mountainside at 1200 feet, mostly covered in mature woodland which needs serious attention. At least half needs felling and replanting.

We're building an energy efficient house with the aim to run on wind and solar power. We have used our own wood as much as possible in the building. We don't want to install a conventional septic tank system, preferring compost toilet and reed bed, but Building Regulations insist otherwise.

We have no mains water, but our own well – which dried up in 1995. We are, therefore, considering digging swales to help hold the water at the highest point of the land. In winter we have a lot of water flowing through the land and plan to harness it via micro hydro for extra power when most needed.

The food garden progresses slowly, due mainly to lack of knowledge and time – the house is taking priority. We have established the beginning of a forest garden which will be added to gradually. We decided on a 30 foot polytunnel which proved a great success, especially as we are quite high and therefore colder. A great added benefit was that we used most of the polytunnel's area in the first year as a kiln to dry the converted wood. Excellent multiple use! Unfortunately, the heavy snowfall this winter collapsed and ruined the tunnel – after the wood had dried – think again.

Naturally, we've discovered that things happen very slowly. At times I feel we've achieved little of what we intended; at others I realise we've done a lot, but perhaps they were things which were not planned or foreseen. It's a learning process that seems will never end.

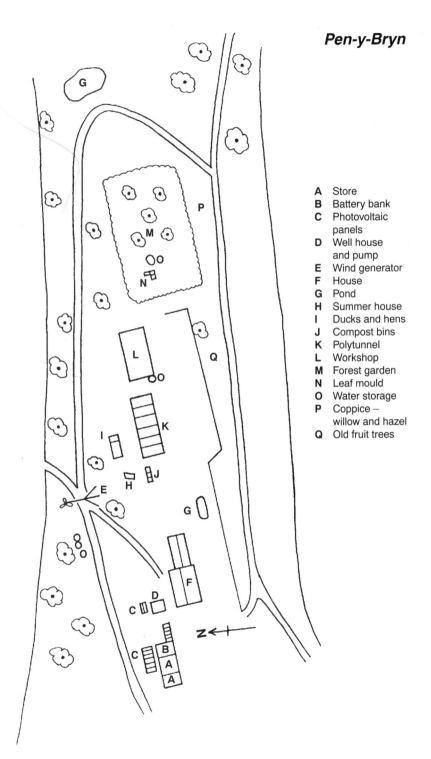

Pen-y-Bryn

A Store
B Battery bank
C Photovoltaic
    panels
D Well house
    and pump
E Wind generator
F House
G Pond
H Summer house
I Ducks and hens
J Compost bins
K Polytunnel
L Workshop
M Forest garden
N Leaf mould
O Water storage
P Coppice –
    willow and hazel
Q Old fruit trees

19

Tyn-y-Fron

Address
*Tyn-y-Fron
Maengwynedd
Llanrhaeadr Y.M.
OSWESTRY
Shropshire
SY10 0DE*

Telephone
(01691) 780540

Fax/E-mail

Contact
Pen Strange

Date est.
1983

Size/acres
6

Residents
4

Visitors
No thanks

About four of our six acres were planted with native tree species in 1984: that leaves two paddocks where we graze a pony, a young orchard (just beginning to crop well if we get the pest control right) and a large garden. Our original design was basically sound, but a) if I'd known more about fencing, there would be more straight lines and right angles in the way the land is divided; and b) the garden we first attempted was too big. We planned to earn money selling organic vegetables, but we now earn money working away from home, so only need enough garden to keep us in vegetables and look good. Our big polythene tunnel has many uses: early spring crops, cucumbers etc. in summer, late salads, drying onions etc. and winter storage (e.g. hay). We keep a few ducks and chickens and have three ponds.

The attached greenhouse all along the south side of the house is a real asset, warming the house quickly from any sun, keeping winds off, providing space for overwintering plants, starting seeds and cuttings, growing tomatoes and leaving wet wellies and coats.

We have no mains services. Our water comes from a spring pumped by a hydraulic ram. There is an outside toilet with a bucket that gets emptied round the fruit trees and bushes, but we are planning an inside toilet soon. Two woodstoves heat the house. After a long wait, we are now in the process of planning and installing a wind generator system to replace an old diesel generator.

20

Chicken
Shack

Chicken Shack is a housing co-op and perma-culture site in mid-Wales. We moved into our property (Bryn Llwyn or Bush Hill) in August 1995. Supported by Radical Routes and funded through Triodos bank and our own loan stock issue, we house eight people in one house and two cottages. Six of the eight people (four men, four women) have taken a 72 hour permaculture design course and our aim is to implement a design on the site to include both the land, the organisation of the community and our individual lifestyles.

We spent our first six months organising our homes (Zone 0), observing the land and looking at how we work as a team – meetings and work designs. Set in four acres in Snowdonia National Park, 50 miles north of Aberystwyth, we have one wet and one dry(er) field and a small patch of woodland. We are aiming to grow some of our own vegetables and to experiment – we are particularly interested in developing a domestic reed bed and compost sewage system.

We are part of a wider community which has grown up around the Centre for Alternative Technology and has its own LETSystem and exchanges of labour and resources. We are presently host to the national administrative office of the Permaculture Association (Britain) and have a resource bank of information on permaculture.

Address
Bryn Llwyn
Rhoslefain
TYWYN
Gwynedd
LL36 9NH

Telephone
(01654) 711655

Fax/E-mail
pcbritain@
gn.apc.org

Contact
Rachel Banks

Date est.
1995

Size/acres
4

Residents
8

Visitors
BA

21

Tir Penhros Isaf

Address
Tir Penhros Isaf
Hermon
Llanfachreth
DOLGELLAU
Gwynedd
LL40 2LL

Telephone

Fax/E-mail
pcbritain@
gn.apc.org

Contact
Lyn, Chris &
Sam Dixon

Date est.
1985

Size/acres
7.2

Residents
3

Visitors
See box

Tir Penrhos Isaf is a seven acre holding in Coed Y Brenin in the Snowdonia National Park. When we bought it in 1986, it was an over grazed, close cropped sward with little variety under scattered mature trees. Any wet areas were damaged by poaching, dry areas succumbed to drought.

We lived four and a half miles from the land until 1991; not ideal. During that time we began the implementation and evolution of our permaculture design, (specifically, Zones 3, 4 and 5). Much of this was fencing and hedging to exclude grazers from some areas. This allowed natural regeneration which was mind-boggling and an excellent teacher, (*Permaculture Magazine* vol. 1.2 winter 92/93).

After lengthy but fruitful discussion with the National Park we acquired planning permission to live here in 1991. Obtaining this was not easy; we learnt a great deal about the application procedure and the planners learnt about permaculture design. We were assisted in a friendly and professional manner.

Because our plot is now our home we have been able to devote more time to the place. Feral deer were the main consumers of our first food-growing on the site. We now have a deer-proofed, intensive, perennial, forest garden, sheltering raised annual beds which are more productive and easier to garden each year.

Through our design we are stabilising and building soil, conserving water, encouraging diversity of habitat, thus providing niches for various flora and fauna, growing food and eating it (them), using sustainable sources of energy, evolving a sustainable system for horses, learning and teaching... We focus our attention on yields that we find easy to sustain and wherever possible trade and exchange locally for what we don't produce ourselves. We are fortunate to be part of a diffuse community of like minded people.

Due to Lyn's recent serious illness we will not be holding courses or receiving visitors this year, (1996). Her recovery is progressing well and we hope to resume both courses and visits in 1997 .

Although some people do live at the Centre, it is not principally a community and you can't just go for an informal visit. It is open to the public all year round as a demonstration centre of sustainable technologies, but you have to pay to get in. There's a lot to see so give yourself plenty of time for a day visit. Some things are not on display to the general public, notably the various sewage treatment systems, phone in advance and make an appointment to be shown round (ask for Peter Harper or Chris Weedon).

If you really want to stay for a while, the only option is by coming on a course or through becoming a volunteer. The courses usually last a weekend, are very intensive and very good. They very nicely complement the typical content of permaculture design courses – much more detailed and of course much more expensive! Write for a leaflet listing courses, dates, prices etc.

Volunteering comes in several varieties:

- Weekend groups are self-catering and cost nothing. You do a day's heroic slave labour and get a morning of being shown around. It makes for a hearty and informative weekend, but you'll need at least 6 people.

- Short-term volunteers stay one or two weeks and do whatever is needed at the time - but don't expect any fancy windmill stuff, it's nearly all weeding and digging holes.

- Long-term volunteers stay for 6 months and are attached to a particular department. Limited places, so a lot of competition, but if you can get in on one of these slots it's excellent training.

If you can't visit, there's a big range of publications broadly along permaculture lines, with strong emphasis on energy. Write for publications list. CAT is one of the oldest and largest 'plots' in this book, with a lot of experience under its belt.

WALES/ BORDERS

22

Centre for Alternative Technology

Address
Centre for Alternative Technology Llwyngwern Quarry MACHYNLLETH Powys SY20 9AZ

Telephone
(01654) 702400

Fax/E-mail
(01654) 702782 cat@gn.apc.org

Contact
Peter Harper

Date est.
1974

Size/acres
40

Residents
15

Visitors
Anytime; BA for volunteers

Y Felin

Address
Y Felin
Melinbyrhedyn
MACHYNLLETH
Powys
SY20 8SJ

Telephone
(01654) 702718

Fax/E-mail

Contact
Liza & Tom
Brown

Date est.
1992

Size/acres
7

Residents
2

Visitors
BA

Have we really been here three years now? How time flies. It often seems that not much has been achieved of our ambitious plans, until we take stock of the changes that is. Certainly things have not happened as planned, but then that's how it should be if you take time to observe the land and listen to its message.

We are self-sufficient in veg now, with the poly-tunnel being a great asset for growing winter salads. A mixed orchard is well established and various other fruit trees and bushes have been planted around the gardens. Logs inoculated with shiitake and oyster fungus have fruited well this year, with much of the crop being dried for winter use. Beehives have increased from two to four and in addition to keeping us supplied with honey, provide us with a popular product for sale on the local LETS market. Four ducks provide us with eggs (some of the time!) and do a great job of controlling slugs in the veg gardens, whilst Branwen and Caradog, the geese, work at keeping the grass down.

Work on renovating the cottage continues and we look forward to being out of the caravan and living in the cottage come summer. An environmentally sensitive, energy efficient building with soul has been our objective. We've used our own timber for rebuilding the roof, a wood block floor and other work, using its natural form and grain as a finish. Also traditional lime mortar/plaster with goats hair has been used and wherever possible recycled or local materials.

We have much enjoyed having visitors who have helped in getting things done and having camping groups to stay in the riverside meadow and circle dances on the grass. A Wales permaculture gathering has become a regular event now on the weekend nearest the summer solstice. All are welcome.

On the list of jobs to be done, besides gardening and finishing the cottage, are 700m of fencing, building a compost toilet with a cob built 'throne house' and getting our spring water system sorted out. There is always plenty to do and offers of help are much appreciated.

Y FELIN.

TOM. 95.

24

Maen
Offeiriad

Address
*Maen Offeiriad
Whitechurch
Crymmych
Dyfed
SA41 3SE*

Telephone
(01239) 891472

Fax/E-mail

Contact
*Annie Whiteley,
Matt Kempster*

Date est.
1995

Size/acres
5

Residents
6

Visitors
BA, May-Oct

Maen Offeiriad is an embryonic permaculture smallholding of 5 acres and 6 sheltered fields situated on a slight north facing slope on the Preselis. The grassland is poor but there are beautiful diverse hedgerows including several mature trees.

Since moving here in December 1995 we have renovated the main house for two parents and have been joined by two more adults. We are now rebuilding a small barn with an attached passive solar greenhouse for our living space. We have a community vegetable garden, a young forest garden, a productive poly-tunnel, compost loo, a lot of willows, two Welsh cobs (one trained to harness) plus a cart, 20+ chooks (free range), one mice-eating dog and a midget cat.

Plans for the future!

- A walled garden, built with building rubble.

- Hedgerows extended with even more trees and shrubs.

- At least four ponds.

- Pigs, bees.

- More comfrey and more willow for basketry and furniture making.

- Existing grassland changing to grow more herbs, rye and clover.

- Windpower for the caravan and the barn.

- Reduce our need to use the car.

- Grow figs, lemons, peaches, kiwi fruit etc..

- To become as self-reliant as possible while working with Nature but still leaving time to be creative and have fun!

Erw Dêg

Address
Erw Deg
Cwm Cych
NEWCASTLE
EMLYN
Dyfed
SA38 9RR

Telephone
(01239) 698370

Fax/E-mail

Contact
Tony Wrench,
Jane Faith

Date est.
1990

Size/acres
1.5

Residents
4

Visitors
BA

We have been here for 6 years now, sometimes with Jane's two daughters and sometimes without. This place is very secluded, lots of wilderness with a bungalow, two dens and a dojo. A lean-to provides solar showers in summer. Most lighting is from photovoltaics and a small wind generator. Our compost loo works well and deters foxes so we have a fine flock of very free range chickens and ducks. We earn money by playing music in a circle dance and ceilidh band, woodturning (Tony) and psychotherapy (Jane), trade in LETS quite a bit and enjoy a simple life.

Our bills are very low. Last year we sold the car and bought an electric 3-wheel milk float which is proving a cheap and tough workhorse. We are in our third year of learning Welsh, the main language spoken round here. We grow a fair proportion of our staple foods and have some good fruit trees and bushes coming on. Last year's best wines were currant and blackberry/ elderberry and it was the first year of our own grape wine. This year we are determined to grow more than 4 carrots, so we welcome helpers in the garden.

The house is designed to be largely run on home-produced timber. It incorporates a Kachel-oven for background heat and other stoves for water. Drainage is separated to black and grey water – the former goes to a bark pit for composting, the latter out into the fields, possibly later into willow coppice.

The land is mainly degraded grazing, half of which has been separated into fenced paddocks, capable of carrying stock – a local organic Highland cattle farmer keeps his animals on it in return for meat. In the other half we have dug two ponds one of which is fed by a lazy swale system. The wet ground surrounding the swales and ponds has been planted with 2,500 willows including some short rotation coppice varieties to provide fuel for the Kachel-oven.

A polytunnel has been erected, fruit trees planted and vast storage sheds erected to contain the expected produce. Bizarrely, the polytunnel remains empty, while the sheds are now filled to overflowing with exotica such as broken axe handles, mouldy hay, odd sized timber and mysterious metal objects. This exciting observation is expected to shortly provide us with many niche marketing opportunities.

Chicken and pig systems are the next projects, while this summer we'll be concentrating on growing food in the polytunnel and perfecting our breaststroke in the ponds. Bring swimming costumes!

26

Gelli Ddewi Isaf

Address
Gelli Ddewi Isaf
Parc y Rhos
Cwm-Ann
LAMPETER
Dyfed
SA48 8EA

Telephone
(01570) 423065

Fax/E-mail

Contact
Ali Kaye,
Nathaniel Holt

Date est.
1991

Size/acres
30

Residents
3

Visitors
BA

27

Dyfed Permaculture Farm Trust

Address
*Bach y Gwyddil
Cwmpencraig
Drefach Felindre
LLANDYSUL
Dyfed
SA44 5HX*

Telephone
(01559) 371427

Fax/E-mail

Contact

Date est.
1995

Size/acres
20

Residents
4

Visitors
BA

Dyfed Permaculture Farm Trust is a new venture to try out, promote and practice sustainable ways of living. The farm has been an organic smallholding for the past 20 years. It is about 500 feet above sea level with lovely views of wooded valleys below. The farmhouse, longhouse and parcels of land have been purchased by four members of the Trust. The Trust itself has the remaining two outbuildings, 3 acres of woodland and six fields totalling 15 acres. Forty people loaned or donated money to purchase the land and are thus Trust members. There are trustees and a management committee. The Trust is hoping to attract more full or associate members, so that we can pay off loans and free up resources for improvements to the site: showers, composting toilets, roof repairs, tree planting, ponds etc. So, if you'd like to become a member, it's not too late and your contribution would be most welcome!

We are now starting to develop the site following permaculture principles. A business plan and design will enable the farm to evolve in an integrated, sustainable way. As time passes there will be more food produced on site to supply camps/courses and locally. This year we hope to:

- Install a ram pump to divert spring water to new ponds.
- Build a low impact/eco-den for long term volunteers.
- Run a few camps/courses.

The permanent dwellers will also be undertaking major building works which will incorporate solar panels, compost toilets and greywater treatment systems.

We hold working weekends by arrangement (usually last weekend each month) and hope to soon join WWOOF when we have more dry, warm spaces to welcome people! We look forward to old and new faces, exchange of ideas and music around the fire.

The inside of Sian's polytunnel with solar bath tub – 'heaven'!

Address
*Upper Ffynnonau
Colva
Newchurch
Herefordshire
HR5 3QX*

Telephone
(01544) 370222

Fax/E-mail

Contact
*Dominic Poelsma,
Anne Adams*

Date est.
1991

Size/acres
6

Residents
2

Visitors
BA

General description: height varies from 380-420 metres above sea level, most steeply sloping. Harsh climate with short growing season, high rainfall (1015-1145 mm annually) and exposure to strong winds. Soil acidic, much of the natural vegetation is bracken with rough grassland, not cut since fenced about 15 years ago. Some mature larch trees from what was probably once a plantation, scattered with a dozen oaks, rowans, sycamore and horse chestnut.

Zones: depend on topography; house is at one end, not in the middle!

Zone 0: household – farm cottage and buildings being renovated. Rainwater from roof of greenhouse, electricity from wind generator and solar voltaic cells. Human waste recycled for garden.

Zone 1: patches of vegetable garden separated from house due to use of yard and track by farmer. Land mulched heavily annually. Good crops of broad beans, runner beans, mange tout peas, onions, spinach, fir potatoes, leeks, turnips, marrows. Salad crops in greenhouse, also a vine with grapes! Herbs in pots outside. Large comfrey beds; green manure used in autumn. Border of tyres filled with soil to act as a barrier to grass coming in, perhaps deter slugs from coming in, confine rampant perennials, protect less rampant ones and enable type of soil needed to be controlled.

Zone 2: fruit and nut trees, shrubs with flowers and berries for birds and insects.

Zone 3: willow (*Salix viminalis* varieties) for firewood, baskets etc., hazel for coppice, elder, blackthorn and hawthorn for birds. Larch plantation, part of which has now been felled and timber used in building.

Zone 4: about 2,000 native broadleaves and Scots pine planted 1991 and 1992 with Forestry Commission grant. Some now 20 feet tall (alder, birch and rowan).

We aim to grow crops in harmony with nature and encourage wildlife, especially in Zone 4.

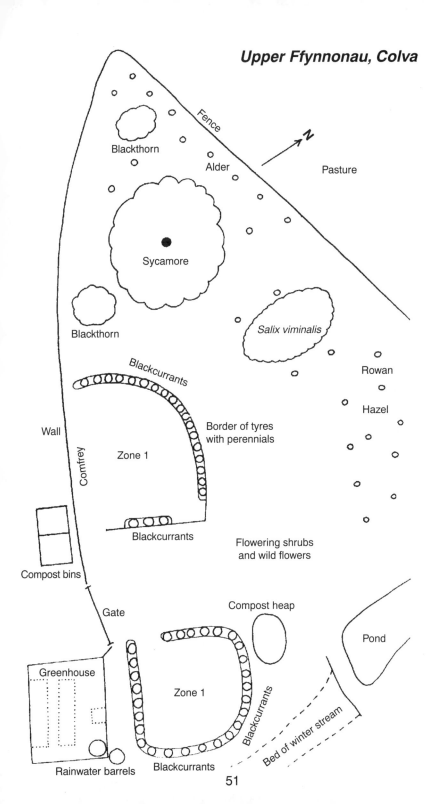

Upper Ffynnonau, Colva

Fence

N

Pasture

Blackthorn

Alder

Sycamore

Blackthorn

Salix viminalis

Rowan

Hazel

Blackcurrants

Border of tyres
with perennials

Wall

Comfrey

Zone 1

Blackcurrants

Flowering shrubs
and wild flowers

Compost bins

Gate

Compost heap

Pond

Greenhouse

Zone 1

Blackcurrants

Bed of winter stream

Rainwater barrels

Blackcurrants

29

Primrose Farm

Address
Primrose Farm
Felindre
BRECON
Powys
LD3 0ST

Telephone
(01497) 847636

Fax/E-mail

Contact
Paul Benham

Date est.
1988

Size/acres
6

Residents
2-3

Visitors
BA, WWOOF

The main income for mortgage, bills, improvements etc. is derived from the 1 acre organic market garden with 4 polytunnels (£10,000-12,000 per year). A very wide variety of vegetables, fruit and herbs are grown. The crops are all reared from seed on the farm and the produce is sold locally; most direct to the consumer from the market stall or via the box system. A wholefood shop and a number of high class hotels are also supplied. The holding has always been run using ecological principles. The very high labour demands have been partly instrumental in discovering permaculture since it became obvious that my energies were not an unlimited resource.

There are four specific permaculture areas. Systems A and B form the one-third acre Forest Garden. System A contains a high density of tall canopy trees which were planted 10 years ago and so this area will be heavily shaded when mature. In System B, there is only one main line of tall canopy down the north side and the canopy drops gradually to the asparagus bed on the south side. Thus more light penetration will be possible in this system. System C will always have good light penetration. In System D the open canopy beneath the young native trees is being utilised for a few years growing mint and annual crops. There are now 80 different varieties of fruit and nut trees and probably as many herb plants.

A flock of 19 Jacob sheep graze the pasture land and provide income. Khaki Campbell ducks help the slug problem by foraging in the garden in the winter. A large pond for the ducks and two small ones for frogs have been created and a bog area is being developed.

A more holistic side to the farm is now developing, with spiritual and healing energies being encouraged. The main focus is with voice through chant and sound and regular sessions using tone, chant, sound and movement are held. Festivals and seasons are celebrated using sound to highlight the energies of the times of year and to connect with the elements and other aspects of the environment. A sacred grove of trees has been planted and a sacred sound chamber is under construction. A round house for communal space and workshops is planned.

System D at Primrose Farm.

30

Riverside Community Garden

Address
*South Riverside
Community
Development
Centre
Brunel Street
South Riverside
CARDIFF
CF1*

Telephone
*(01222)
387269 Michele
220309 Centre*

Fax/E-mail

Contact
*Michele
Fitzsimmons*

Date est.
1995

Size/acres
0.01

Residents
None

Visitors
BA with Michele

REACT (Riverside Environment Action), a group of Cardiff residents, developed the community garden at the South Riverside Community Development Centre over 18 months from early 1994 to mid 1995. Where a barren, lifeless, uninteresting space existed there is now a vibrant, lush urban oasis with a pond, borders, containers and marsh areas full of trees, shrubs, herbaceous perennials and self-seeders. There are over 70 species, the majority of which are edible and native to Europe, many with multiple uses. Habitats have been designed into the space enabling a variety of animals to thrive who in turn help look after the garden. A lot of the area is brick pavers where children can ride their tricycles and adults can sit around and enjoy a breather from the office.

The garden is surrounded on three sides by high walls, with the Centre itself making the fourth side. The walls provide a microclimate for the garden by acting as a heat store and by sheltering the garden from winds. They also cause extremes of sunny and shaded areas and provide vertical growing space. A key design feature is the watering system. Two 40 gallon water butts have been placed on a purpose built platform adjacent to the mezzanine landing of the stairwell. Water from the roof goes into the butts and is fed via hoses to a combination drip and sprinkler system. The provision of a timer allows for the watering to be conserving of human energy too.

Another key but invisible part of the design is the people side. Twelve pupils from St Mary's Primary School worked with permaculture designer Michele Fitzsimmons to create the design and the selection of plants. Soil was placed in the beds by Community/ Probation Services and the stairwell containers were made at their workshops. The TaffWestLETScheme has been used to good effect. The 15 foot pergola crossing the garden was built for LETS as was the illustrative guide. REACT itself is a group of Cardiff residents who have all put in many hours of voluntary work to get the garden to where it is now.

The work on the garden has been documented on video which is available to groups with similar projects and will be especially useful to permaculture educators.

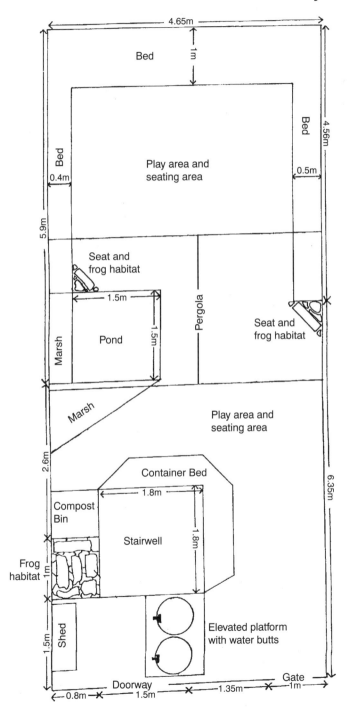

31

Aberdare

Address
*Blaennantygroes
Farm
Cwmbach
ABERDARE
Mid Glamorgan
CF44 0EA*

Telephone
(01685) 877885

Fax/E-mail

Contact
*Tony & Verity
Newman*

Date est.
1993

Size/acres
15

Residents
5

Visitors
BA

In late December 1993 we moved into 15 acres of wildness and wet. As we unpacked we flattened the boxes, laid them over the huge weeds in the barely visible front garden and covered them with muck. Later we planted potatoes, our first crop. This pattern of reclamation has been similar all around the house. In the side garden we cut down bramble and put in chickens. After they dug and manured the patch we came in with mulch and potatoes. Half this garden was reclaimed last year with keyhole raised beds. We made a cold frame from a uPVC door and a greenhouse from hazel benders. Paths are made with old carpet/cardboard/newspaper overlaid with straw or hay. The animals provide a ready supply of muck and straw. The ducks have helped enormously with slugs.

We applied for grants for hedgelaying and woodland extension. The hedges were laid last year and work on the wood is underway. This mainly entails fencing off an area to exclude livestock for a period. Pioneer woodland is already advancing across old pasture. The plan is simply to assist natural regeneration, only planting if necessary. Host trees such as mature oak and ash should provide enough seed.

The rear field is being 'left alone'. A helpful man from the NRA described it with great enthusiasm as a valuable wildlife habitat. I had seen only a problem, but have been assisted to see it as a paradise!

At present we have cattle, sheep, pigs and ducks. The whole venture is new to us. We have remained consistently (if not constantly!) cheerful. We have lots of plans. We are always happy to receive help and advice and happy to offer it to anyone else starting up. We are very happy to share our mistakes!

The sewage systems at Oaklands Park and others built along the same lines are compatible with many of permaculture's ethics. What makes it all the more interesting is that the ideas were developed by NASA and the Max-Planck Institute. However, a more expected bedfellow, biodynamics within Camphill Communities, has developed the idea to make it practical, reliable, beautiful and practically odourless. Oaklands Park gave Uwe Burka a mandate to correct the sewage systems since they were discharging above their consent. Water authorities eventually gave their blessing for a system in Uwe's garden but not without reluctance: sewage treatment has mainly been mechanical or chemical in recent years. The idea that a garden full of plants might do the job all year round as well or better was an about turn to be taken only after much thought.

The first system was a series of four terraces set into the landscape. Each terrace held sand and stones to a depth of 40cm. Growing in this medium are reeds, bulrushes, iris and sedges. The sewage solids are settled and the liquid effluent is distributed over the surface of the first terrace and moves vertically through the bed. The liquid coats each grain and pebble in a thin layer, while the gaps between the stones contain oxygen to feed the microorganisms that detoxify the liquid. Oxygen is replenished by the plants' roots. The final effluent is of EC bathing water quality.

However, the organic load that entered is still present in the water, better called nutrients. In the systems currently being designed, withy beds are created to receive this irrigation. In the biodynamic philosophy it is advised not to use this to grow human food. To extend the cycle between human shit and human food is considered important, but to grow trees that also clean the air is fine.

The success of the first system has led Uwe to build another at Oaklands Park for 100 people. There is now a company, Camphill Water, to design and build these systems for others willing to take on the challenges of looking after a system. The skills are those of a caring gardener rather than an engineer – cutting the plants once a year and changing the flow from one part of the first terrace to another every so often to allow the former to dry out – to remineralise.

32

Camphill Water

Address
Camphill Water
Oaklands Park
NEWNHAM
Gloucestershire
GL14 1EF

Telephone
(01594) 516063

Fax/E-mail
(01594) 516821

Contact
Mark Moodie

Date est.
1985

Size/acres
160

Residents
90

Visitors
BA, 1st Mon of month at 3pm

Ragman's Lane Farm

Address
Ragman's Lane Farm
Lower Lydbrook
LYDBROOK
Gloucestershire
GL17 9PA

Telephone
(01594) 860244

Fax/E-mail
(01594) 860123

Contact
Matt & Jan Dunwell

Date est.
1990

Size/acres
60

Residents
5

Visitors
BA, WWOOF

We have a 60 acre mixed stock farm, mainly under grass at present. Our aim is to find ways of making traditional grassland systems more sustainable. We are also slowly taking land out of grassland to be put to more productive uses.

Things to see and work to do!

- Direct marketing of meat with customer involvement in the farm.
- Working towards self-sufficiency in animal feed especially with comfrey for pigs.
- Ceramic stoves (Kachelofen) built by Reinhart von Zchock.
- Artist blacksmith's forge.
- 1 acre vegetable CSA project/two polytunnels.
- 3 acre chestnut plantation.
- Retort charcoal kiln producing BBQ and drawing charcoal and soil improver.
- Half acre fish pond with chinampas – growing willow for artist charcoal and baskets.
- Converted barn for residential courses (composting loo, ceramic stove, green oak conversion, suitable for B&B and holidays too).
- 7 acres of woodland including coppicing of hazel, ash and elm in conjunction with the Coppicing Association.
- DIY solar panels/solar house design.
- Cob barn wall built in 1993.

Please phone for further information on courses that are available.

Our meat, veg and fruit are sold direct to customers in Bristol, Gloucester and the Forest of Dean. This is one of the main permaculture principles of the farm but largely invisible to visitors. Selling direct has a fundamental impact on the nature of producing food. It encourages diversity, as you are looking for a harvest over a long period. It also confronts the issue of transport. We mainly deliver into Bristol, a distance of 30 miles, modest in comparison to the distance most British produce travels let alone imports. Customers buying through a box system are encouraged to eat with the season and this makes an enormous difference to the average 'Food Miles' in our weekly shopping.

Mandy Pullen's Box System garden at Ragman's Lane Farm.

Rose Garth

Address
Rose Garth
Storridge
MALVERN
Worcestershire
WR13 5EL

Telephone
(01886) 880849

Fax/E-mail

Contact
Paul Millsom

Date est.
1989

Size/acres
5.5

Residents
5

Visitors
BA

The plot is generally southeast facing on a steep slope with a yellow clay subsoil, but sunlight exposure is reduced by the high tree covered hill opposite. The house (c.1840) is situated on the lowest corner of the land, by a major road. No permaculturist would build a home here considering the reduced sunlight, car pollution and poor scope for aquaculture, but the original occupants were interested in roadside custom. A good stand of established oak and birch lines the top third of the land.

Our first three years were the dry hot summers and so the few trees that were planted had to be tended well. Brambles emerged almost everywhere and these have proved to be a great asset. The masses of blackberries are utilised and the foliage provides perfect conditions for natural regeneration and tree shelter. Even an apple has seeded in the protection of the bramble.

Planting started in earnest in the winter of 1991/2 and now exceeds 1,000 trees. The land is now surrounded by woodland (wild cherry, wild pear, wild service, chestnut, hazel, whitebeam and oak). A conspicuous forest garden (1/4 acre) is noticed from the road. A less densely planted rear garden has beds for annuals and space for chickens. In the centre of the woodland is a densely planted orchard with over 30 varieties of apple, plus pears, plums, damsons, cherries, pea trees, 'sweet' oaks, chestnuts, cobnuts and mulberries.

An arboretum boasts butternuts, walnuts, strawberry tree, hackberry, raisin tree, Russian olive, persimmon and honey locust.

Energy self-sufficiency is a challenge considering the age and situation of the house, which is mainly heated by wood from the plot.

There is now a considerable surplus produced on the site, particularly fruit. This is available to anyone who wants to come and help harvest the surplus.

35

Earthworm

Earthworm took over Wheatstone in 1989, the buildings had been vandalised and the seven acres left untended. The design, size and age of the house affords neither easy repair and maintenance nor ecological efficiency. We ceased using flush toilets in 1991 and have built a series of vaulted compost loos.

We adopted a more permaculture approach in 1992 after hosting a design course, starting a new kitchen garden nearer the house and growing more perennial crops. We mulch extensively with straw and cardboard. We operate a traditional organic bed system with herbs, companion flowers, dwarf fruit trees and soft fruit alongside the annuals. Living in a frost pocket the growing season is short and we rely on our greenhouse and polytunnels.

We have planted a small future woodland of ash, oak, alder, willows, hornbeam, hazel, cobnut, wild service and sweet chestnut. We're experimenting with commercial garlic and hope to develop a workers co-op market garden. We grow a reasonable amount of vegetables and a good supply of soft fruit but we aren't yet self-sufficient and a lot of the land is not yet reclaimed.

The camping kitchen and field are used for gatherings and courses. As a very cheap venue we'd like to see more use of our extensive (but basic) facilities. We don't keep food animals. The communal diet is predominantly vegan, as is the farming. We use compost, mulching, comfrey, liquid feeds and green manures to maintain fertility. We believe effective recycling of human wastes to be of great importance. The community runs on a co-operative basis with decisions and responsibilities shared. We have regular WWOOF and visitor weekends.

Address
*Earthworm
Housing Co-op
Wheatstone
Leintwardine
CRAVEN ARMS
Shropshire
SY7 0LH*

Telephone
(01547) 540461

Fax/E-mail

Contact

Date est.
1989

Size/acres
7

Residents
13

Visitors
BA, WWOOF

36

Highwood Hill

Address
Highwood Hill
Rushbury
CHURCH
STRETTON
Shropshire
SY6 7DE

Telephone
(01694) 771342

Fax/E-mail

Contact
Robert Hart

Date est.
1985

Size/acres
1

Residents
1

Visitors
BA

The primary aim of the Forest Garden scheme on Wenlock Edge is to demonstrate a system which would enable a family or community to achieve a degree of self-sufficiency in food, herbs and small timber throughout the year. While the forest garden areas, comprising shade-tolerant fruit, nut, herb and perennial vegetable plants, constitute the heart of the system, other areas are designed to utilise the full potentialities of the site:

1. Open areas, for sun-loving vegetables and herbs.

2. Wetland areas, for plants that grow in water or bogs, including a reedbed system for purifying effluent.

3. Container areas, for plants in tubs, e.g. 'patio garden', 'bedsit garden'.

4. Big tree area, for trees that will grow too large for a forest garden.

5. Willow coppices, cut for basketry, shredded for compost.

6. Small greenhouse.

As far as possible, the whole scheme complies with three 'forest principles':

- The soil is kept permanently mulched with organic hay, straw, grass cuttings or compost and is undisturbed.

- Multiple cropping is practised in all areas.

- Aromatic plants are grown to purify the atmosphere and ward off pests and diseases.

The scheme also includes a small Ecological House with wood-burning stove, organic loo and wind generator for lighting. (See *Forest Gardening* by Robert A. de J. Hart, Green Books, 1991, available from Permanent Publications).

In 1992 the Forest Garden received more than 450 visitors from 26 countries, many of them drawn by the article in *The Permaculture Plot*. Most of them expressed keen interest and many expressed a desire to establish similar schemes. I regard the Forest Garden as a link between the international permaculture movement and the international Agroforestry movement, whose head-quarters are the International Centre for Research in

Agroforestry (ICRAF), Nairobi, Kenya. I would much like to see close liaison between the two movements, in particular 'twinning' between permaculture groups and forest garden communities in tropical areas.

The original Forest Garden: old pear tree surrounded by herbs and red,white and blackcurrants and raspberries.

MIDDLE ENGLAND

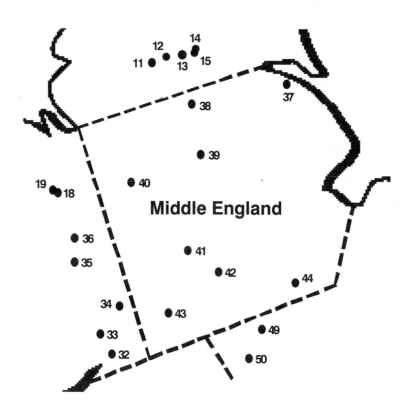

37 Hardy's Field, Barrow-on-Humber
38 Quaker Community, Bamford
39 New House Farm, Kniveton, Ashbourne
40 Fordhall Farm, Market Drayton
41 Ashram Acres, Birmingham
42 Ryton Forest Garden, Coventry
43 Evesham
44 West Wood, Bedford

We have a 3.25 acre plot on the outskirts of the village of Barrow-on-Humber. It has been organically managed for the last 16 years but always on a part-time basis as we have always been in some kind of paid employment too. When we took it over there were three trees and acres of twitch; we were the original 'Good Lifers' and over the years have had cows, pigs, sheep, goats, children and poultry. There was always more work than time so it was with a sense of relief we discovered the permaculture way of doing things.

In spring 1995 we had a permaculture design drawn up by Lynch & Goldring in the hope of making the plot more sustainable. There is no less work to be done in setting up the system but there is a coherence to what we do now that has increased the pleasure already and will ultimately decrease the workload too.

We have now an established orchard and four plot rotation vegetable garden, worm beds, chickens and 357 more trees planted since 1979. We are planning to grow vegetables for the local box scheme or to swap produce for weeding on our LETS. We know that four course rotations are not strictly orthodox and that vegetables in rows are now out of order but change has to be gradual and I'm afraid there's still nothing that makes my heart swell as does a lovely line of blue-green leeks.

Self contained projects within the whole that we hope to complete during the next year are:

- The building of a solar greenhouse.

- A compost toilet for the guest caravan.

- Establishment of a willow plantation.

- An improved sitting out area.

Visitors are welcome through the WWOOF scheme or through HolidayLETS.

37

Hardy's Field

Address
1 College Road Barrow-on-Humber N Lincolnshire DN19 7ED

Telephone
(01469) 530792

Fax/E-mail

Contact
Sue & Dave Stephenson

Date est.
1979

Size/acres
3.25

Residents
2

Visitors
WWOOF

38

Bamford

Address
*The Quaker
Community
Water Lane
Bamford
SHEFFIELD
S30 2DA*

Telephone
(01433) 650085

Fax/E-mail

Contact
John de Carteret

Date est.
1988

Size/acres
10

Residents
20

Visitors
BA, WWOOF

The land and buildings were formerly used as clay diggings, a dump site for building rubble and clogged filter sand, a railway and the offices of the Severn Trent Water board. Our project has been the formation of a Housing Co-operative, the conversion of the buildings to living accommodation and the rehabilitation of the land.

We now have a mixed woodland, managed for fuel and wildlife, a willow wetland coppice, a wildflower meadow area, three annual vegetable plots with raised beds and an emerging forest garden. There is much scope for continued application of permaculture principles. We have two goats and plan to keep chickens. We are currently planning to divert all roof water into a new pond which will provide water for all growing areas.

We are establishing a resource centre where people can get close to and learn about nature. Part of our nature trail is wheelchair accessible and a composting toilet is soon to be completed. Working weekends are held on the first and third weekends of each month – enquiries by post only please, including SAE.

T his is a small family farm on carboniferous limestone, overlain by clay loam of depths 2-3 feet, depending on the gradient. There are Bronze Age burial mounds, medieval ridge and furrow, a lead mine, lime kiln and quarry. Most of the farm is permanent grassland, most of it still recovering from 1960s inputs of herbicides and fertilisers. The aim is to produce a herb-rich sward with no inputs apart from manure return and occasional calcified seaweed. Other livestock feed inputs are minimised to avoid transport and use of 'third world' inputs.

The general environment is being re-diversified to benefit wildlife. Two acres of broadleaved trees have been established, including fruit and nut trees with fruit bushes under and some islands of vegetables. Vegetables are grown in the garden on beds and winter crops in a polytunnel.

The own-root fruit tree project will based here from Spring 1996. The project is based on the findings of Hugh Ermen, formerly of Brogdale, whose work over many years showed that own-root trees have many benefits - there is no incompatibility between scion and stock, leading to fruit quality of the very highest, with the best flavour and potential storage life. With adequate pollination fertility is very high and it is probable that self-fertility is increased. General health is improved and some problems, such as brittle wood, disappear. The only disadvantage is that most varieties left to their own devices will make vigorous, unproductive trees. This tendency is curbed by bringing the tree into bearing as quickly as possible, using a range of traditional techniques – summer pruning, tying down etc.

New House Farm will be home to the ORFT tree nursery and some trial plantings. At 750 feet above sea level it is a little too high for most fruit trees, but fine for raising trees. The marginal altitude should be useful for comparing the performance of grafted and own-root trees of the hardiest varieties.

Long term WWOOFers are accommodated here in caravans. Long term plans include solar/wind power, a new wetland area and coppicing.

39

Kniveton

Address
New House Farm
Kniveton
ASHBOURNE
Derbyshire
DE6 1JL

Telephone
(01335) 342429

Fax/E-mail

Contact
Bob & Mary
Smail

Date est.
1993

Size/acres
40

Residents
5

Visitors
BA, WWOOF

Address
Fordhall Farm
MARKET
DRAYTON
Shropshire
TF9 3PR

Telephone
(01630) 638255

Fax/E-mail

Contact
Arthur Hollins

Date est.
1946

Size/acres
150

Residents
1

Visitors
BA

The First World War brought the farming community a false prosperity with a large increase in the use of fertilisers to produce extra food at home. A reduction in the animal population and the vast increase in fertilisers started a downward trend in soil fertility. When hard times came in the 1920s and 30s, there were financial difficulties with fertiliser firms; then a gradual restriction in everything that aided soil fertility. In these sandy, sloping fields, which were bare during the winter, soil bacteria soon began to die away. The slopes became thinner and sandier and the best soil was washed to the bottom of the field. All this broke Father's health and he died when I was only 14. Taking on a run down farm at this age, seemed very enormous for me; but the alternative was even worse. I was convinced I could restore the old fertility.

The rotation that has gradually developed achieves a complete coverage of all the field and provides adequate food for all the year round open air feeding for over 100 cattle and 100 sheep lambs; it has slowly eliminated all corn growing, cash root crops and root crops for our cattle. Our rotation is achieved by carefully resting and rotating our field pastures to produce winter grazing on a 3 year cycle. The mixture used for these pastures includes rye-grass, cocksfoot, timothy, fescue, clover, chicory, sheep's parsley, kidney vetch, yarrow and nettle. November to December grazing is achieved by resting 50 acres from mid-August; January to early February grazing by resting 50 acres from the end of August, which is fertilised with all farmyard manures available and, if necessary, some organic fertilisers. Seed is cast onto flattened molehills and spread around by the animals, through their manure or on their claws. Each field received one of these winter grazings every 3 years. We eliminated the need to return any fields to a root break for autumn and spring grazing.

The advantages with our grass rotation system are that the fields are never bare. These rotations help to eliminate plant and animal diseases. We think the battle for good health both in plant and animal is fought in the top two inches of soil with the larger animals and micro-organisms. The whole area in the early autumn and spring is one vast turmoil with an up and down battle going on between all sizes and types of animals, bacteria, fungi and micro-organisms, the farmer using balanced rotations to nurse and study these cycles that go on in the soil.

We have spent 15 years studying a 1/8 acre plot that was laid down to study what happens when our farming system of permanent cover is compared with a plot where seed is sown on sterile sand and shale. The plot had all the soil removed, then seeded with all kind of grasses, herbs, sand-dune grasses and weeds and then covered with one-inch square nylon mesh. It took about 7 years for most of the seed to germinate – the sand dune grasses germinated first and provided the necessary cover. No manures were added, it was left entirely to nature. Most of the grasses are now fully established and the soil insects are there in normal numbers, followed by moles. The most exciting result is that 2.5 inches of good quality loamy soil and roots is now established on top of the nylon mesh, in only 18 years.

Under the foggage system the amount of soil that has come all over my farm must be even greater. Modern systems of cultivation create a similar result but in the other direction; 2.5 inches is lost forever and brings in the need to feed the land, even organic arable land. This also accounts for the plants on our farm always having their main new roots on the surface under the leaf cover; they are following the area of chemical synthesis within the top inch under the protective cover of the plants returning leaf fall, which is occurring all year round. The importance of this cannot be over estimated. We are seeing the reality of soil production instead of steady permanent soil erosion; the insects do it for us.

We are now in the process of developing a machine we've called 'the Culturseeder' so that permanent cover can be achieved with all arable land anywhere in the world, crops can be grown in a real sustainable system with a steady rise in fertility, cutting completely the need for fertilisers, lime, pesticides etc.

As farmers, we can only guess at what really goes on and judge from what appears to bring results, balancing the needs of all our plants and animals with the elements, assisting nature in her struggle to produce a surplus and using that surplus for raising our standard of living.

41

Ashram Acres

Address
Ashram Acres
23-25 Grantham
Road
Sparkbrook
BIRMINGHAM
B11 1LU

Telephone
(0121) 773 7061

Fax/E-mail

Contact
Judith Weltman

Date est.
1981

Size/acres
0.5

Residents
5-20

Visitors
BA, WWOOF

This three-quarter acre garden was created from the corner of a ten acre windswept field about 15 years ago. Over the years a substantial windbreak had been created and there are also a number of mature fruit trees and bushes.

During the first year in which a permaculture design was applied to the garden, more windbreak species were planted, together with nut trees and some new exotic plants. Many herbs were introduced and a wildflower area has replaced some of the previously mown grass. It is intended that much of the grass area at present needing cutting should be replaced by shrubs, trees and herbs in the future, gradually reducing the need for grass-cutting machines.

Raised beds and terraced areas have been created to grow this year's vegetables. A pergola has also been constructed and it is intended that the climbing plants will add to the windbreak.

Solar collectors from reclaimed domestic radiators give the household hot water system a welcome boost and the conservatory also adds to household solar gain.

In the field beyond the garden, three acres of trees have been planted. As they grow and create more shelter, more of the field, at present grazed by sheep, may be incorporated into the design.

Future plans include a pond and swale system, to make use of roof water and grey water and the introduction of hens.

Ryton Gardens, the headquarters of the Henry Doubleday Research Association (HDRA), covers 10 acres and includes numerous demonstration plots illustrating themes such as no-dig gardening, organic pest control and composting, together with a shop and restaurant.

It now includes a forest garden plot, which was designed by Graham Bell and is maintained by members of the Permaculture Association. To begin with, the flat site was broken up with raised beds, which were mulched heavily and planted with a number of fruit, nut and ornamental trees. Later, soft fruit, other bushes and herbaceous plants were added, a process which is continuing, as are the handweeding and mulching needed to ensure that the public see the acceptable face of permaculture.

The plants in the garden have all been donated, whether by commercial nurseries, individuals or the HDRA itself, and they range from the usual apples, soft fruit and herbs to more unusual species such as hybrid hazels, azeroles, oca and Good King Henry. While the garden is still sunny and open, annual vegetables are also being grown, but as the canopy closes there will be more call for shade-lovers. The plants are in the process of being labelled.

The garden relies entirely on volunteer labour, workdays being held on Saturday or Sunday once a month or so. At the same time it functions as an educational resource, and makes a good site visit for permaculture courses. A group called Friends of the Forest Garden produces a newsletter to keep gardeners up to date with forest gardening events at Ryton and elsewhere. Anyone wanting more information should contact Jane Powell, c/o Earthward, Tweed Horizons, Newtown St Boswell's, Melrose, Roxburghshire TD6 0SG. Tel. (01835) 822122 (*see page 18*).

(*see page 18*)

MIDDLE ENGLAND

42

Ryton Forest Garden

Address
Ryton Organic Gardens
Ryton-on-Dunsmore
COVENTRY
CV8 3LG

Telephone
(01203) 303517

Fax/E-mail
(01203) 639229

Contact

Date est.
1993

Size/acres
0.25

Residents
None

Visitors
Anytime; BA for volunteers

43

Evesham

Address
c/o 1 Merstow
Cottages
Merstow Place
EVESHAM
Worcestershire
WR11 4AY

Telephone
(01386) 48448

Fax/E-mail

Contact
John Porter

Date est.
1987

Size/acres
1.25

Residents
None

Visitors
BA

The plot is rectangular, 1.25 acres, flat, with a stream along the NE boundary with associated trees and thick tall hedge next to the bridle way along the NW boundary. It can flood in winter but has land drains. There is a tendency to late Spring frosts.

The plot started as grass. It now has an establishing forest zone – a mix of oak, ash, cherry, hazel, hornbeam, alder – a shelterbelt/fuelwood coppice, a horseshoe shaped orchard/embryonic forest garden enclosing a south facing area of raised vegetable beds, a hazel area for nuts and a wild flower meadow and pond.

Hazels are now productive and I am starting to coppice a few this year. Fruit tree planting is finished for the time being while I add to the shrubs and bushes – blackcurrant and gooseberry. I'm also adding to the climbers. Continental walnut varieties have finally looked alive.

The willow coppice is still being extended. A tolerant neighbour has enabled me to solve the problem of blocked land drains creatively and I'm digging a series of drainage ditches to replace drains through the willow area. I'm beginning to see the possibility of aquaculture sometime in the future. It will be interesting to see if having more water around in ditches will reduce the frost risk (warming the air, draining away cold air?). A major ditch was dug in 1995 to complete drainage improvement. This will need landscaping giving a greater variety of environments and more mulch via reed beds, plus water cress and other aquatics.

Fertility is improving quite quickly due to closed loops for sewage (all mine ends up on the land eventually) and wood ash. Essex red clover provides a lot of mulch, cut several times a year. Meadow provides hay mulch for the forest garden. Wild species of plant and animals are thriving – about 15 species of butterfly, grass snakes, frogs, toads, hare, two types of orchid. All from land that was down to market gardening a decade or so ago. No rabbits yet and the birds only take the first week's crop of raspberries.

W est Wood is a 200 acre ancient wood owned by the Forestry Commission. The canopy was clear felled in the 1930s and replanted with oaks. The understorey and ground flora retain the diversity of an ancient semi-natural woodland. I buy the standing undergrowth and also the oak thinnings and undertake to coppice them and extract the usable material. My main and most profitable product is thatching spars, of which I can generally get about 50,000 from a hectare. These retail at about £60 per thousand. This yield is well below that from prime hazel coppices because the undergrowth is partially derelict and has been locally shaded out during the denser earlier decades of plantation oaks. Improving the productivity of the coppice will be a gradual process of thinning the canopy and increasing the density of coppice stools using natural regeneration and layering. I have accumulated a fair amount of information and experience of these methods and will happily correspond about these and other factors which are important to the success of commercial coppicing including deterring deer browsing, disposal/uses of waste brash, quick and easy bramble control and sensitive ways of keeping rides passable. I produce a whole range of other coppice products including charcoal, firewood, hedging stakes and binders, pea sticks and rustic poles.

I have been experimenting with multistorey cropping, wild foods and no-dig gardening. I have tried acorns (left on the lid of my charcoal kiln overnight), honey fungus, edible ornamentals (day lily, honesty, shepherds purse, hairy bittercress) and leaf curd. I mix the curd with oatmeal, onion and herbs to make 'leaf-burgers'. They are more than just edible; they are actually very pleasant, but require a fair amount of work for the amount of food produced. A much more significant proportion of my food comes from 'carrion' (e.g. road casualties) and from 'gleanings' I have agreements with a local farmer to buy up cheaply the crops he cannot sell because of gluts or slight blemishes. While not strictly permacultural I see this as a stepping stone stage, accustoming my body to a more vegetable based diet and weaning myself off bread, biscuits and choccy bars.

44

West Wood

Address
c/o 15 Rotten Row
Riseley
BEDFORD
MK44 1EJ

Telephone

Fax/E-mail

Contact
Mark Powell

Date est.
1990

Size/acres
200

Residents
None

Visitors
BA

EAST & SOUTHEAST ENGLAND

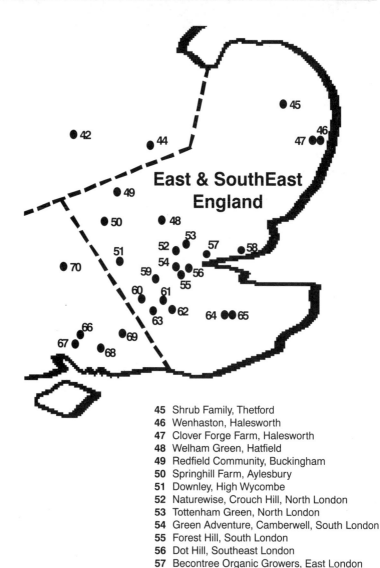

East & SouthEast England

45 Shrub Family, Thetford
46 Wenhaston, Halesworth
47 Clover Forge Farm, Halesworth
48 Welham Green, Hatfield
49 Redfield Community, Buckingham
50 Springhill Farm, Aylesbury
51 Downley, High Wycombe
52 Naturewise, Crouch Hill, North London
53 Tottenham Green, North London
54 Green Adventure, Camberwell, South London
55 Forest Hill, South London
56 Dot Hill, Southeast London
57 Becontree Organic Growers, East London
58 Westcliff-on-Sea, Southend
59 Knollmead Allotments, Kingston
60 Woking
61 Kerhilley, Leatherhead
62 Reigate
63 Abinger, Dorking
64 Brickhurst Farm, Tunbridge Wells
65 Goudhurst, Tunbridge Wells

Shrub family is a well established community in SW Norfolk. We are housed in a grade two listed farmhouse that has been around in various incarnations for at least 400 years. It's not built in the grand manorial style – very much an artisanal home with correspondingly thin walls, draughty doors and no need for any refrigeration in the winter! The community is small – at present 6 adults and 5 children – almost full (but always room for good energy). We are not income sharing and have no communal businesses – most members work. We do share communal tasks in the house and gardens and co-operate strongly domestically, socially and in areas like childcare.

We have about an acre of land with about a third of it under cultivation, including a 60 x 16 foot polytunnel. The garden is run on a 'low-external input' basis – deliberately avoiding emotive terms like 'organic', 'biodynamic', 'permacultural' etc. hopefully drawing on all good practice as far as knowledge, time and energy allow. There are strong permacultural strands guiding our approach to land use and living, but we are decidedly not 'permacultural obsessives', taking the view that we need to develop our own systems appropriate for our own situation and that these systems need to evolve from use and custom rather than 'grand design'. We are currently developing soft fruit areas and a circle garden, as well as running 'mainstream' vegetable/herb/flower plots and polytunnel. There's always plenty to do in the garden and we welcome working visitors.

Our wider concern is putting the 'suss' into sustainability – how do we take the values an virtues of the community out to meet that big wide world? We believe that as a community we have the potential to grow and aim to convert to a housing co-operative using the equity and income of the community to expand. Our bigger, long term, dream is to establish an 'eco-village', working on the principle that demontration is one of the best ways of encouraging change. We have both practical and theoretical expertise in the issues surrounding sustainability and welcome debate, discussion and possible co-operation with individuals and groups.

45

Shrub Family

Address
*Shrub Farm Cottages
Larling
East Harling
NORWICH
NR16 2QT*

Telephone
(01953) 717844

Fax/E-mail
(01953) 717474

Contact
Tim Bastable, Molly O'Brien

Date est.
1991

Size/acres
1

Residents
11

Visitors
BA

46

Wenhaston

Address
Rose Cottage
Blackheath
Wenhaston
HALESWORTH
Suffolk
1P19 9HD

Telephone
(01502) 478257

Fax/E-mail
(01502) 478257

Contact
Bryn & Simon
Raven

Date est.
1995

Size/acres
0.5

Residents
2

Visitors
BA

Both of us are members of the East Suffolk Permaculture Group. Bryn's main interest is in how best to transform our half acre garden into a self-sustainable organic system. Simon is more interested in the 'people care/fair shares' aspect of permaculture (e.g. developing our local LETScheme) which has sometimes resulted in his not taking sufficient account of supporting Bryn's 'earth care'. Consequently our principle activity so far has been in sorting out Zone 00!

Our garden is on a south facing slope with the house placed inconveniently at the bottom end. The soil is extremely light – basically sand. So far we have begun to turn the vegetable plots into a forest garden by planting numerous fruit and nut trees and beginning the task of losing our previously regimented lines of vegetables. Most recently work has begun on rationalising Zone 1 by introducing a new mulching bed along the length of a long established lawn. This too is becoming smaller as other encroachments are being made. Water preservation and distribution is a major issue for us and we are in the early stages of making the necessary changes to this system as well.

All of our efforts rely upon the support and encouragement of the group as a whole. Through regular meetings, the sharing of information, planning visits to each other's sites and working parties, we have developed a co-operative spirit which we would be happy to share with anyone interested in starting a similar group.

47

Clover Forge Farm

Until the middle of 1994, Clover Forge consisted of four acres of bare pasture. No trees, no shade, no food. Heavy, waterlogged clay which set hard as concrete in the summer. The 100 year old wooden bungalow was draughty, leaky and overrun with rodents and arachnids!

Ideally, we would like to have demolished the buildings and rebuilt with improved design and materials. However, financial constraints dictated we 'go with what we've got'. We both work (one full time and one part time) and so, although there is some money to pay the mortgage and fund the project, there is only one person working part time on the site. I find I get a lot of help from other permaculture enthusiasts in our local group and I'm hoping to get WWOOFer help soon.

The aim is to reach a design stage of inter-connectedness and high productivity (food and medicinal herbs) within five years – to provide an example of permaculture in Britain – to reduce our reliance on outside income. In Zone 0, the space and water heating is provided by a wood burner. A rescued cat is keeping the 'wildlife' out of the house. Many improvements are currently underway. In Zone 1, raised beds get the plants off the heavy clay and a polytunnel (recycled) extends the season. This area contains food, herbs, flowers and recreational space for adults and children.

In Zone 2 a forest garden is integrated with chickens and stables. Zone 3 is a standard orchard (which will one day graze small livestock underneath), a large pond (which has yet to be integrated into the design) and a bonfire site for those festive occasions. This leaves about 2.7 acres of pasture for the cart horse and Shetland pony, both of which provide transport, labour, manure and leisure. Already, we have abandoned supermarkets and are getting more productive all the time. So, although we are a transitional site, there is much to see. Long-distance visitors are welcome to camp.

Address
Clover Forge Farm
Cratfield Road
Huntingfield
HALESWORTH
Suffolk
IP19 0QB

Telephone
(01986) 798112

Fax/E-mail
cre4@student.open.ac.uk

Contact
Cindy & Rick Engel

Date est.
1994

Size/acres
4

Residents
4

Visitors
BA, WWOOF

48

Hatfield

Address
6 Nash Close
Welham Green
HATFIELD
Hertfordshire
AL9 7NN

Telephone
(01707) 276754

Fax/E-mail

Contact
Michael & Julia
Guerra

Date est.
1991

Size/acres
0.015

Residents
2

Visitors
BA

We live in a new-built ground floor flat with garden on three sides. In our small rear and side areas we have managed to grow about 30 varieties of fruit, over 60 herbs, almost 20 sallets and about 50 other different vegetables. We try to ensure constant ground cover especially around the fruit trees and herb beds. We also grow a number of perennial and annual pollen plants amongst all the beds and have a small pond with frogs. Slugs are still a slight problem and we have to resort to the manual method, but as we grow everything within 10m of our back or front door this is not a problem.

Our raised beds are made of old railway sleepers and the paths are the remnants of the patio that covered the whole back area. The beds were filled with a mixture of composts and manures with some sharp sand, as under the paving is consolidated sand with cement on top of heavy clay. We are new gardeners and are learning fast. Even so we manage to keep our food bill down to around £3 each week for 6 months without starving, which is just as well because we are both unwaged.

A typical weekend on this 'commuter' estate consists of people mowing, planting herbaceous borders with annuals and washing cars. We do not own a car, but most of our neighbours do and most of them enjoy racing up and down our close. All in all an unfriendly site for permaculture – it required two very polite, explanatory and firm letters concerning our land rights, our plans and permission to implement them from the site developers to prevent our upstairs neighbour mowing our area of herbs, wildflowers and 'ground-breaking' plants (potatoes). In their opinion they were unsightly and untidy weeds.

We would like to experiment with growing a few grains: amaranth, quinoa or oats etc. But most of all we would also like to grow more perennial vegetables. We only spend about 2 hours a week doing any work (not including construction projects – which only amount to a morning at any time). It is a shame that we will probably not be staying here much longer, but we have plans to reproduce – and we could use a little more room!

6 Nash Close, Hatfield

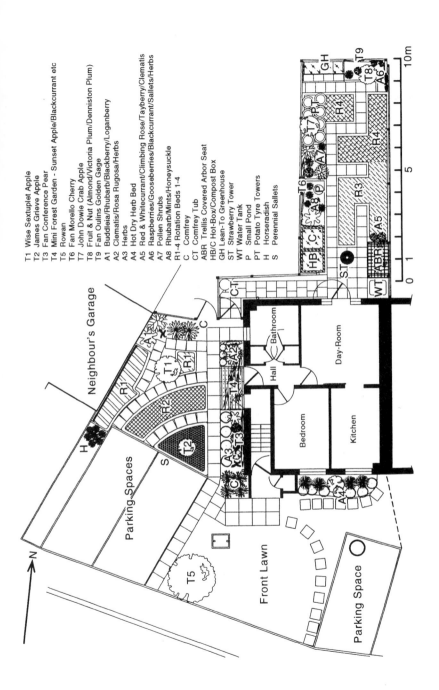

T1 Wise Sextuplet Apple
T2 James Grieve Apple
T3 Fan Conference Pear
T4 Mini Forest Garden - Sunset Apple/Blackcurrant etc
T5 Rowan
T6 Fan Morello Cherry
T7 John Dowie Crab Apple
T8 Fruit & Nut (Almond/Victoria Plum/Denniston Plum)
T9 Fan Oulins Golden Gage
A1 Buddleia/Rhubarb/Blackberry/Loganberry
A2 Clematis/Rosa Rugosa/Herbs
A3 Herbs
A4 Hot Dry Herb Bed
A5 Red & Whitecurrant/Climbing Rose/Tayberry/Clematis
A6 Raspberries/Gooseberries/Blackcurrant/Sallets/Herbs
A7 Pollen Shrubs
A8 Rhubarb/Mints/Honeysuckle
R1-4 Rotation Beds 1-4
C Comfrey
CT Comfrey Tub
ABR Trellis Covered Arbor Seat
HB/C Hot-Box/Compost Box
GH Lean-To Greenhouse
ST Strawberry Tower
WT Water Tank
P Small Pond
PT Potato Tyre Towers
H Horseradish
S Perennial Sallets

79

49

Redfield

Address
*Redfield
Community
Buckingham Road
Winslow
BUCKINGHAM
MK18 3LZ*

Telephone
(01296) 712161

Fax/E-mail
*(01296) 714983
106031,2416@
compuserve.com*

Contact
Simon Pratt

Date est.
1978

Size/acres
17

Residents
25

Visitors
BA, WWOOF

There is considerable support for permaculture here and a fair amount of what we have been doing here for the last 18 years is moving towards sustainability for this site.

- We grow a proportion of our own food organically, over 50% some years, including fruit, vegetables, eggs and meat.
- We supply most of our firewood needs and have planted over 2000 trees in recent years.
- We reduce our impact on the earth's resources by sharing our lives together; one kitchen and one laundry for 30+ people, on site waste water treatment, composting of household wastes.
- We share transport where possible, have most goods delivered and organise weekly shopping trips for the whole group.
- Many of us work from home or in the local area.
- We reduce our need for external income by growing food and doing our own maintenance.
- Most of our social needs are supplied from within the group, including childcare, entertainment, practical and emotional support.

We are planning to convert our large stable block into more living and working space, both for community members and outside users. The materials used will be as green/ecological as possible and we intend to make the whole building energy efficient with a high degree of insulation and other features such as solar panels and compost toilets. We hope this development will be a sustainable model for the next century, by combining housing and workspace on the same site.

We have allocated two acres of our field for an organic vegetable and fruit production scheme supplying food at reasonable prices to local people. All we need now is an experienced grower to run the scheme! We expect these developments to bring closer connections with the local community, which is also happening through the Local Agenda 21 process.

We are organising a straw bale building workshop in the autumn, one of a number of events in the *Redfield Centre*. Send for details.

Above: Redfield residents and friends plant 700 trees in one weekend in February 1995.

Left: Bob's garden with rhubarb, gooseberries and young plum tree.

50

Springhill

Address
*Springhill Centre
Cuddington
Road
Dinton
AYLESBURY
Buckinghamshire
HP18 0AD*

Telephone
(01296) 748278

Fax/E-mail
*(01296) 748360
deltatech@
tcns.co.uk*

Contact
*Hugh Coates,
David Francis*

Date est.
1990

Size/acres
140

Residents
8

Visitors
BA, WWOOF

Springhill Farm is set in the attractive valley of the River Thame and has been organic since 1946. Some years ago it was redesigned on permaculture lines with extensive tree planting which will in the future provide timber, shelter for animals and crops and essential habitat for wildlife. An agroforestry project is supervised by the Open University. Several springs provide irrigation for the land and fresh water for residents.

The farm is also the home of the Springhill Centre, a registered charity acting as a resource and study centre to help patients with chronic disability or life threatening illness to research and direct their own illness management. Farm diversification includes a seasonal restaurant and a farm trail.

Community Supported Agriculture is now established and we currently have 70 households subscribing to a share of the annual harvest. Shareholders pay a quarterly or monthly subscription in return for fresh vegetables and fruit delivered each week to a number of distribution points. The subscription covers the cost of growing the produce and developing the scheme, provides employment for the growers and contributes to helping us safeguard the countryside, its plants, birds, animals and way of life for future generations.

The main vegetable area forms part of a large plum orchard and here we are growing on permanent beds, some of which are located between the rows of plum trees which afford shelter from the prevailing winds. Seedlings are raised in a heated greenhouse and there are three polytunnels in which early and non-hardy crops are grown. Wild fruits such as elderberry, blackberry and rose hip, as well as some of the Victoria plums, are freely available on a pick-your-own basis to subscribers.

Current projects include barn restoration for use as a meeting place, a new hen house, a reservoir in the plum orchard combined with a low energy pumping system to irrigate the vegetable beds, a wildlife habitat and recreational area.

Most of my time has been spent on the house, which needed a new more efficient gas boiler, hot water tank and thermostatic radiator taps, damp proofing of lower back walls below soil level, resurfacing of balcony and elevated path to back garden. The attic and walls required insulation, windows were already double glazed. The whole house needed redecorating and much repair.

Compost bins, a tumbler and worm bin were installed early on to take a large amount of material needing clearing – five large unproductive trees, suckering sumach and kerria, strangling bindweed and cleavers and a neighbour's overhanging trees. These have been cut back to create a relatively sunny glade with woodland edge in the north facing back garden.

Many fruit trees and shrubs along with herbs, vegetables and traditional cottage garden and wild plants have been planted through mulch. Pumpkins and sweetcorn have been most prolific. Most of the fruit trees and climbers are being trained up the recently erected fences. The ponds are partly dug. Rain water butts were put in at an early stage at the back and front of the house as well as on the balcony and have proved most useful whilst establishing plants in our dry summers. The greenhouse has been put in a sunny spot at the bottom of the garden against a wall. The balcony has provided almost all our salad, herb and strawberry needs during the summer, with ample space left for lounging in the sun.

If I come up on the Pools I'll put in solar panels, a glass porch on the sunny side and a wood burning stove before finding a rural retreat and starting all over again!

E & SE ENGLAND

51

High Wycombe

Address
Three Doves
41 Partridge Way
Downley
HIGH WYCOMBE
Buckinghamshire
HP13 5JX

Telephone
(01494) 534198

Fax/E-mail

Contact
Daphne Watson

Date est.
1990

Size/acres
0.06

Residents
4

Visitors
BA

Naturewise

Address
Naturewise
Crouch Hill
Recreation Centre
Hillrise Road
LONDON
N19 3PT

Telephone
(0171) 281 3765

Fax/E-mail

Contact

Date est.
1991, 1995

Size/acres
0.2, 0.5

Residents
None

Visitors
BA

Naturewise started the first public urban Forest Garden in Britain in 1991 on a 0.2 acre plot at Crouch Hill in North London. The land was given by the Parks and Recreation Department of Islington Borough Council. Backed by grants from Islington for a feasibility study it was shown that in an area of high unemployment people were worried about their food and the use of pesticides where children played.

We have made an edible landscape providing a model of an urban environment that can produce its own food. This garden cost £5000 and took many hours of voluntary labour. On a south facing slope below a plastic football pitch and above a council estate, bushes and herbs are planted in guilds on terraces irrigated by swales. Paths following desire lines are marked by steps and wood chippings. We experiment with well-researched fruit varieties and rare berries, with composts and mulches – which we find essential as there is no source of water nearby.

The first phase of the project was prepared by participants on a permaculture design course and planted in Spring 1992. The second phase was prepared and planted in 1994. We were inspired by Robert Hart's work on developing small ecologically sustainable gardens for suburban plots. The first phase of our Forest Garden was planted according to Robert Hart's book *Forest Gardening*. The second phase aimed at increasing biodiversity and maintaining rare species. This garden is open to the public all the time and we are very willing to show visitors around and can arrange lectures and tours.

In 1995 we began to extend a depleted orchard to make a second Forest Garden. It consists of nearly 0.5 acre in the Margaret McMillan Day Nursery on Hornsey Rise. They have over 200 children, among them a proportion of disabled. This garden can be visited only by special arrangement.

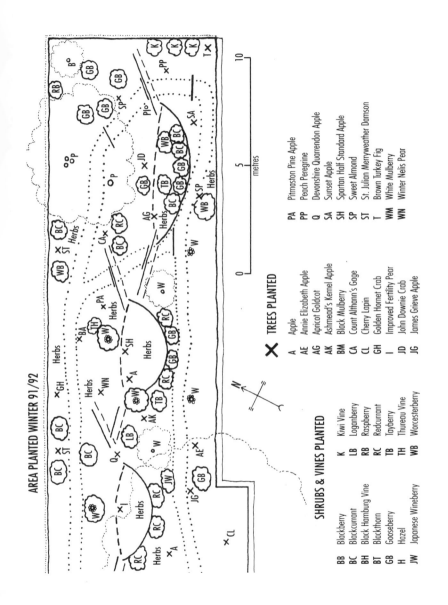

AREA PLANTED WINTER 91/92

SHRUBS & VINES PLANTED

BB	Blackberry	K	Kiwi Vine
BC	Blackcurrant	LB	Loganberry
BH	Black Hamburg Vine	RB	Raspberry
BT	Blackthorn	RC	Redcurrant
GB	Gooseberry	TB	Tayberry
H	Hazel	TH	Thureau Vine
JW	Japanese Wineberry	WB	Worcesterberry

X TREES PLANTED

A	Apple	PA	Pitmaston Pine Apple
AE	Annie Elizabeth Apple	PP	Peach Peregrine
AG	Apricot Goldcot	Q	Devonshire Quarrendon Apple
AK	Ashmead's Kernel Apple	SA	Sunset Apple
BM	Black Mulberry	SH	Spartan Half Standard Apple
CA	Count Althann's Gage	SP	Sweet Almond
CL	Cherry Lapin	ST	St. Julian Merryweather Damson
GH	Golden Hornet Crab	T	Brown Turkey Fig
I	Improved Fertility Pear	WM	White Mulberry
JD	John Downie Crab	WN	Winter Nelis Pear
JG	James Grieve Apple		

N

0   5   10

metres

53

Tottenham Green

Address
15 Jansons Road
LONDON
N15 4JU

Telephone
(0181) 211 0159

Fax/E-mail

Contact
Judith Hanna

Date est.
1994

Size/acres
0.01

Residents
2

Visitors
BA

An ornamental-edible urban terrace house garden, running east-west on clay loam. Just over grown grass when we moved in, it now boasts a small wildlife pond, which had its first frogs the second weekend after it was dug and a lean-to greenhouse against the rear of the house. The first summer, we grew and supplied more edible weeds, veges and herbs than we could eat, with surplus for the freezer to carry us over winter. This second summer, we're encouraging selected self-seeding. Our mini-orchard includes a dual-variety cherry tree, redcurrant, blackberry, three minaret apples and a minaret pear. With no space to spare for compost bins, 'in situ compost heaps' with cucurbits grown on top, are the solution we've adopted.

We keep a worm bin beside the back door which, with local recycling banks, keeps our weekly garbage down to one swing-bin bag. The garden supports a rich supply of earthworms, earwigs, ants, gastropods, ladybirds, hoverflies, assorted bees etc.. At the end of the summer we had three freezer drawers stocked with home-grown veges and we were harvesting more than we could eat from July through September. Most productive were the nine runner bean plants and a single spaghetti marrow vine. With both of us employed full-time, it has all been done by weekend pottering, plus the occasional summer evening picking session and quick morning patrol. It has hardly felt like work at all.

Sustainable and enjoyable living in one of London's most densely built and poorest areas is as much our concern as simply gardening. We're located handily for public transport links, on what is designated as part of London's 1,000km cycle network and we have co-ordinated National Bike Week/Green Transport Week local action. We are part of North London LETS and regularly supply a herbalist on the system with her raw materials. We've become part of the local council's 'tree warden' scheme. We are also co-ordinating work to create a community wildlife garden and environmental information centre in a derelict old school yard on nearby Tottenham Green. These 'sustainable living' activities are all as important to urban permaculture as what can be seen in the garden.

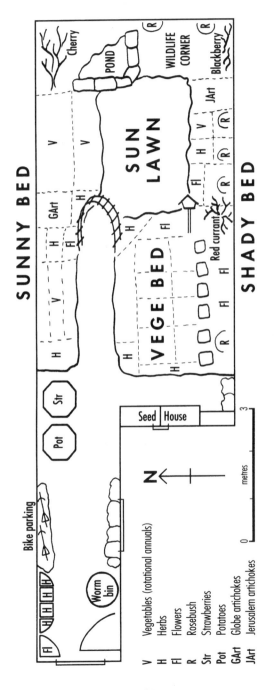

SUNNY BED

SHADY BED

SUN LAWN

VEGE BED

Cherry

POND

WILDLIFE CORNER

Blackberry

JArt

Red currant

Bike parking

Worm bin

Str

Pot

Seed | House

N

metres

0   3

V   Vegetables (rotational annuals)
H   Herbs
Fl   Flowers
R   Rosebush
Str Strawberries
Pot Potatoes
GArt Globe artichokes
JArt Jerusalem artichokes

54

Green Adventure

Address
*54 Camberwell
Business Centre
99-103 Lomond
Grove
LONDON
SE5 7HN*

Telephone
(0171) 277 2529

Fax/E-mail

Contact
*Stefania, Viv &
Bola*

Date est.
1996

Size/acres
0.5

Residents
None

Visitors
BA

An orchard in the middle of the city isn't every one's idea of a healthy food source by any means, but this isn't the main reason for choosing to plant fruit trees rather than the usual selection of ornamentals found in parks.

This is an aesthetic and air improvement proposal but mainly it is a permaculture project designed to involve the local community in the creation of sustainable environments, of thinking about where our food comes from and how it can be grown organically, easily and pleasantly.

The site of the Community Orchard is currently a grass area with seven small trees, surrounded by a health centre and business centre, the Camberwell Magistrates Court, housing estates and sheltered housing. The site, given over to the community to cultivate, will no doubt be used as a leisure space by local residents and passers-by and such a project could have all sorts of ramifications. It will be a chance for local citizens to creatively become involved in Local Agenda 21 issues in a direct, wholly practical and experiential way.

Apples, pears, plums and cherries are obvious candidates for planting and the land could easily take 15 trees, more if dwarfing rootstocks are also used. Species like mints, strawberries, chamomile and other herbs give visible results in the same year and provide interesting ground cover and so are being planted first. We have visited other permaculture plots for tips and design/varieties suggestions and more regular trips for interested residents are planned for the future.

Given the nature of the project and the desirability of precisely such initiatives as London edges towards being a sustainable city, it should be easy to attract the minimal funds needed for tools, trees and bushes. It is also quite possible that as individuals become involved, the idea of 'planting and looking after your own tree' will catch on. Ideally locals will feel this is their land and our 'design idea' is that the forest garden should grow organically and 'naturally' according to the contributors' own design ideas and aesthetics, not ours. Down with 'experts'!

A moderate sized, south aspect garden on the shallow south facing slope of Forest Hill, one of the hills that form the edge of the Thames Basin in South East London. The soil in the area has grown from London clay beds and in this particular garden has been covered with junk and then with a layer of clay spoil from excavations. There has been some use of specific herbicides in one area.

The design for the back garden, to complement a sensitively managed house, was initiated by the owners of the property, Nick and Gina, facilitated by us. The emergent design was an urban forest garden with 13 fruit trees on varying root stocks and a varied under-storey as forage for young Mark, some herbs and food for the kitchen, and provision for wildlife habitats. The first part of the installation was about improving the soil by combating compaction and adding organic material alongside a programme of worm encourage-ment, and getting the trees in.

Nick and Gina decided to move up Forest Hill away from main roads and traffic and rented the house and garden to us, hoping that we would have the expertise and care to keep the garden going. When we moved in the garden was dominated by a wide variety of apple, pear and plum trees, some soft fruit bushes, some herbs and salads and patchy topsoil. The pond was filled with blanket weed and frogs.

The installation work continues with more perennial plantings, the establishment of more salad and herb beds and more top soil building. Organic material is coming from local stables, neighbours' compost contributions and mulch crops in the garden. Worm encouragement continues using yeast extract and shredded newspaper.

We are not planning to become self-sufficient from the garden, instead we will use it to supplement food that we buy in from our local box supply scheme run by members of South East London Permaculture group. We believe that in the urban environment garden agriculture will only get us so far down the path to sustainability, and the application of permaculture design to other areas of life is equally important.

55

Forest Hill

Address
167 Dartmouth Road
Forest Hill
LONDON
SE26 4RQ

Telephone
(0181) 699 0389

Fax/E-mail
pcbritain@
gn.apc.org

Contact
Carl Smith,
Nicci Del Rio

Date est.
1994

Size/acres
0.05

Residents
2

Visitors
BA

56

Dot Hill

Address
c/o 9 Bournewood
Road
Plumstead
LONDON
SE18 2AX

Telephone
(0181) 855 2868

Fax/E-mail

Contact
David Goodfellow

Date est.
1992

Size/acres
1.2

Residents
None

Visitors
Anytime

The Dot Hill Forest Garden is a London Wildlife Trust (LWT) Nature Site. It is managed by local people and members of the Greenwich Nature Conservation Society, who have an informal agreement with LWT. It is ex-allotment land, adjacent to active allotments, a park and a housing estate. Natural succession from open cultivated land into woodland has created an interesting mosaic of plant communities. This forms the basis of the forest garden with many fruiting trees and shrubs: apples, pears, damsons, crabs, hips, haws, elder, raspberries, blackberries, currants, gooseberries and grapes. Other useful plants include hops, horseradish, burdock, dandelion, nettle, plantain, cleavers and comfrey. This forest garden has established itself through neglect!

As the site is essentially a nature conservation area there have been few introductions, particularly of alien species. However, in order to increase yield and quality of fruit, pruning and other seasonal management is carried out. We are looking forward to some good crops although local kids prefer using unripe fruit as missiles and then refreshing themselves with expensive sweets. We are running courses on forest gardening using the site as an example and are trying to involve people living nearby in our activities; so far we have seen a lot of net curtain twitching but little else.

Urban permaculture has some very challenging aspects, with many open spaces being vulnerable to the forces of entropy (vandals, developers, politicians etc.) and require a subtle design approach to create inconspicuous, resilient and productive growing areas. The Dot Hill site is a good example of this and should continue to thrive as a wildlife and community resource.

The site is owned by the London Borough of Greenwich Leisure Services and held under license by the London Wildlife Trust. Access is open, so the site can be visited freely. It is located on Dot Hill Road, Plumstead, London SE18. Shrewsbury Park is on the opposite side of road. The site is 0.5 mile South of Plumstead Common. Pedestrian access is from Dot Hill Road, an unmade road suitable for motor vehicles, between Garland Road and Plum Lane. Grid reference TQ 443 773 (OS 1:50,000 sheet 270).

B econtree Organic Growers is a co-partnership of local people formed to revitalise an over grown site, formerly the grounds of a small church which was destroyed in an air raid in 1944. The land is next to allotments which were in production during the war when the 'Dig for Victory' campaign was in full swing. This campaign helped Britain feed itself when food imports were blockaded.

Working with nature is a traditional part of allotment keeping and by following permaculture methods, BOG will be able to work to the London Ecology Centre's Agenda 21 Network on environmental initiatives in the capital. We hope that authorities and local planning decision makers will recognise our efforts and adopt us as a model to assist others in the community who may wish to implement Agenda 21. We aim to fulfil 98% of the criteria by:

- *Reusing and recycling resources:* Composting, trenching and soil conditioning by natural means.
- *Saving energy:* Solar heating, greywater and water catchment tanks.
- *Cultivating local land:* Allotment keeping.
- *Monitoring the local environment:* Looking at local flora and fauna, their health, breeding patterns and available habitat.
- *Conserving nature:* Protecting natural habitats and avoiding harmful chemicals.
- *Green building and planning:* Community building and self-build projects.
- *Community development and education:* University of East London students are working on surveys and mapping; design students from Barking College have produced logo and leaflet designs; scouts are involved in tasks which help them achieve nature conservation badges; the British Trust for Conservation Volunteers Enterprises, formed with the help of the long term unemployed, is making a strong contribution.
- *Developing the local economy:* LETS, local produce outlets and co-ops have been started up and we have our own swapping system with honey as its main 'currency'.

E & SE ENGLAND

57

Becontree Organic Growers

Address
Becontree Organic Growers 44 Gale Street DAGENHAM Essex RM9 4NH

Telephone
(0181) 592 8941

Fax/E-mail

Contact
Barry Watson

Date est.
1994

Size/acres
3

Residents
None

Visitors
BA

58

Westcliff

Address
*35 Rayleigh
Avenue
Westcliff-on-Sea
Essex
SS0 7DS*

Telephone
(01702) 303259

Fax/E-mail

Contact
Graham Burnett

Date est.
1994

Size/acres
0.1

Residents
5

Visitors
*BA, no accom-
modation*

We moved into Rayleigh Avenue in May '94 and armed with Graham Bell's *Permaculture Garden*, leaflets from Plants For A Future and inspiration from the previous *Permaculture Plot* (especially the projects of the Guerras, the Jannaways and Robert Hart) almost immediately set about developing the overgrown lawn, straight concrete path and flower bed we had inherited.

18 months later, the path has been broken up and used to make stepping stones and rockery; we've planted dwarfing fruit trees and bushes; established vegetable, herb and flower herbs; built a greenhouse; dug a wildlife pond; made a worm bin and built a fence/climbing trellis to keep the children from the pond and more fragile crops....

Although far from full development, yields have included quinoa, carrots, brassicas, squashes, tomatoes, sweetcorn plus plenty of saladings. Also loads of frogs, aesthetic pleasures and learning experiences.... By no means 'self-sufficiency' (is that a desirable goal anyway?), but a valuable supplement to our allotment's output....

Future ideas/plans:
• Schemes for grey water recycling.
• Greater use of vertical space.
• Logs for fungi.
• Bird and bat boxes.
• More sharing of plants, seeds, ideas.
• Communication with neighbours and community.

I'm a vegan-organic gardener and try to recycle as much scavenged urban detritus as possible – glass and timber from skips, old logs, bricks, tiles, wine bottles for bed edging, 5 litre paint tubs for pots, etc., etc., etc.... The compassion of veganism combined with the ingenuity of urban permaculture creates a fruitful 'edge' that will need serious consideration if we are to leave behind old habits and create sustainable, non-exploitative and cruelty free futures for our towns and cities.

Respect and thanks for help and shared skills to: Ron, Gary, Dave, Paul and James. It couldn't have been done without you....

35 Rayleigh Avenue, Westcliff-on-Sea

Before
(May 1994)

After
(September 1995)

Pile of rubbish

Bed with 4 rose bushes

Path (concrete)

Lawn

Concrete area

Kitchen

Greenhouse

Pond

Log

Archway

Lawn/ Children's play area/ Adults chill-out area!

Comfrey

Concrete area

Pots

Bench

Store

Kitchen

Worm bin

Proposed grey water recycling/ reed bed system

N
↑

Trees or bushes

Beds

Climbers

59

Knollmead

Address
*c/o 163 Hook Rise
South
SURBITON
Surrey
KT6 7NA*

Telephone
(0181) 773 2322

Fax/E-mail

Contact
Pooran Desai

Date est.
1990

Size/acres
1

Residents
None

Visitors
*BA, working
Sundays*

Kingston Permaculture was set up in 1992 and was given access to one acre of disused allotments by Kingston Council. A group of volunteers have been working steadily since January 1993, spending alternate Sundays on site, learning together about permaculture and traditional crafts. So far the following have been accomplished:

- Forest garden with over 50 traditional fruit trees.
- Creation of two wildflower meadows.
- Planting 100m of native hedge and *Rosa rugosa*.
- Digging two ponds, one lined with clay from site.
- A shelter with wattle and daub internal walls.
- Construction of a pole lathe and manufacture of turned furniture from trees harvested on site.
- Planting of a willow coppice.
- Building a herb spiral.

The main work is now underplanting and developing vegetable growing. The group is happy to welcome visitors and volunteers, particularly those who want to learn by doing! The group has received support from The Royal Borough of Kingston upon Thames, Barclays/BTCV Community Action, Shell Better Britain, British Gas Grassroots and English Nature.

A Fruit hedge
B Entrance
C Lean-to & pergola
D Shed
E Compost bins
F Vegetable bed
G Herb spiral & lawn area
H Hazel & willow coppice
I Forest garden
J Pond
K Fruit hedge
L Demonstration plots (sunny)
M Demonstration plots (shady)
N Existing hedgerow
O Wild flower meadow
P Beehives
Q Reed bed

Pooran Desai planting up a herb spiral at Knollmead Allotments.

60

Woking

Address
*4 Brynford Close
WOKING
Surrey
GU21 4DW*

Telephone
(01483) 763497

Fax/E-mail

Contact
*David Gearing,
Chris Marsh*

Date est.
1993

Size/acres
0.1

Residents
2

Visitors
*BA, no accom-
modation*

The site is a very ordinary suburban garden. We wanted to create an example of what can be done to produce a variety of food as sustainably as possible in such a situation and in the process to enjoy really fresh organically grown produce, which is not available for sale around here. Sometimes we feel we have not achieved much, but then take comfort from the obvious natural health and diversity of our plot, compared with the highly artificial and inedible landscape around us.

The first six months was occupied with clearing several dense patches of mature decorative shrubs, then clearing some areas of lawn and putting in a wildlife pond, a greenhouse, a fruit cage and pole-and-wire supports for fans and raspberries. Given our environment, we pay some attention to the appearance of the garden and have thus avoided structures made of scavenged materials. However, we have made use of on-site rubble, bricks and recycled planks for bed edges, plastic bottles as plant protectors, old carpet for suppressing grass and ground elder etc..

The design was envisaged as a mini-forest garden, which was consistent with the existing layout, as the growing area was already surrounded and shaded by large trees and hedges. After two years there are about 30 fruit trees and bushes and the plot has produced a reasonable variety of vegetables and herbs. We also grow compost/mulch/ground-cover plants such as comfrey, phacelia, mustard and field beans and decorative/edible/pest-discouraging flowers like marigolds and nasturtiums. We are now trying (with some success) to encourage permanent, self-seeding vegetables and herbs and over-wintering salads and greens.

A forest garden, even a tiny one like this, will take ten years or more to mature into full productivity, but we are very encouraged by our ability to harvest something just about every day of the year and by the spiritual aspect of being able to do something healing on our own unpromising bit of land.

Kerhilley is a house with a large garden – just over 0.5 acre – on the outskirts of a small town in the Surrey commuter belt. We have grown fruit and vegetables here for 34 years by a minimum dig method and without using any artificial chemicals or animal fertilisers since our last chicken died over 20 years ago.

Eight years ago we decided to work towards self-sufficiency in food in the hope of showing that two elderly vegans could produce all the food they really needed from a small acreage with their own manual labour and hardly any bought in materials. It is said that a vegan can live on food from a fifth of an acre. We consider extra ground is needed to grow compost material to maintain soil fertility.

We feel it is wrong to use food from countries where people are hungry: many because they have lost their land to exporters. Moreover locally produced food can be more health promoting. Resources used in preservatives, packaging and transport are saved.

In 1986, inspired by Robert Hart, we started to grow soft fruit and perennial herbs beneath the old fruit and nut trees in the northwest corner of the garden. Hazel nuts, various beans and peas, sunflower, maize and quinoa seeds and potatoes yield ample protein. We grow a great variety of fruits and vegetables, including grapes, tomatoes, peppers, cucumbers and winter lettuce in our two greenhouses. All give some protein as well as vitamins, minerals, trace elements and energy.

We keep the soil fertile with compost and the winter tares that we sow on the ground cleared in the Autumn. We use comfrey liquid fertiliser. We are bringing more land into cultivation each year and now have no doubt that we could achieve self-sufficiency in food if we had the time to give to gardening that we now give to running an educational charity, the Movement for Compassionate Living, the Vegan Way.

We realise that we have much to learn and appreciate the help and encouragement of the permaculture movement. We offer a variety of home produced leaflets and booklets on our work and welcome visitors by arrangement but cannot offer accommodation.

61

Kerhilley

Address
Movement for Compassionate Living
47 Highlands Road
LEATHERHEAD
Surrey
KT22 8NQ

Telephone
(01379) 379382

Fax/E-mail

Contact
Kathleen & Jack Jannaway

Date est.
1958

Size/acres
0.5

Residents
2

Visitors
BA

62

Reigate

Address
The Bungalow
Shagbrook
Main Road
REIGATE
Surrey
RH2 9RE

Telephone
(01737) 248909

Fax/E-mail

Contact
Meike Dalal

Date est.
1984

Size/acres
3.5

Residents
3

Visitors
BA, WWOOF

Originally the smallholding belonged to the head gardener of Shagbrook, a Victorian residence. He was fortunate enough to buy 'his' kitchen garden along with the blue, tree-lined, once exotic walk around the stone-walled pond which led to his orchard.

Unfortunately, the orchard was eroded. That area is now used mainly as paddocks for retired Shetland sheep. The shelter belt at the back was replanted with a variety of trees, a small patch produces enough field crops of vegetables for the house and serves as a commemorative herb garden donated by a worn-out organic gardener.

The small Victorian brick storehouse was converted into a residence in the 1930s and two extensions since then have made it big enough for modern standards.

A constant stream of visitors is attracted by the way of life and the space behind the house. Some of them realise the challenge and responsibility of looking after the land and find it too daunting. Others come and help. Long and short term WWOOFers feel inspired and enjoy the sharing of knowledge, skill, life-skills, time, space and food. There is time to nurture these aspects here. How can permaculture exist without?

Since the Permaculture Design Course held here in August 1991, there are undulating edges, butts full of rainwater, spacious compost loos and various salad plants and herbs nestle successfully under plum, mulberry, quince, cherry and pear trees. Honey is shared with the beekeeper down the road who also gives demonstrations to visitors. Perennial patches of edibles are encouraged to supply their own seedlings and have become well established.

The only poultry possible to keep with so many foxes is confined to a mobile ark but we have a constant harvest of eggs and the manure is spread out.

The next project is about making use of the fleeces and identifying the herbs. Anyone interested and prospective feltmakers please apply.

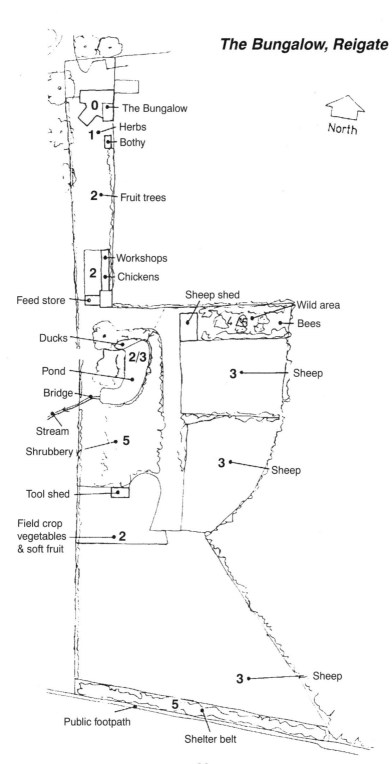

The Bungalow, Reigate

North

0 — The Bungalow
Herbs
1 — Bothy

2 — Fruit trees

Workshops
2 — Chickens

Feed store
Sheep shed
Wild area
6
Bees

Ducks
2/3
Pond
3 — Sheep
Bridge
Stream
Shrubbery — 5

3 — Sheep
Tool shed

Field crop
vegetables — 2
& soft fruit

3 — Sheep

Public footpath
5
Shelter belt

63

Abinger

Address
Sun Cottage
Rad Lane
Abinger
DORKING
Surrey
RH5 6RA

Telephone
(01306) 731272

Fax/E-mail

Contact
Glynis Dallas-Chapman

Date est.
1994

Size/acres
0.16

Residents
2

Visitors
BA

This is a vegan project. When we moved here, the salient features were a large lawn, some young conifers and fruit trees, a sheer 3 foot drop down from the land to the west and areas of erosion of the sandy soil. Tree crops and rabbit wire were priorities. The conifers were exchanged for some extra soil from my neighbour.

In digging up the lawn to back-fill the E-W slope, many buried remains of old buses, bikes etc. were removed, often with a tough, home-made riddle fitted over a wheelbarrow. Simultaneously, the eastern hazel hedge was shore up with spare organic matter. The slope is now less than 1 in 12, much better for fruit trees. Some late keeping top fruit have been specifically selected to overlap with early fruits the following year. Rapid ground cover was particularly helped by fast-growing under-storey crops. Behind our home, the banks remain steep. A series of water butts, shade-tolerant bushes and herbs, logs for fungi and comfrey banks all give protection.

Nitrogen fixers include clover, extra beans, *Caragena arborescens* and *Elaeagnus ebbingei*. One compost bin rotates sites. Future plans? Apricot, sweet cherries and outdoor seedless grapes (Perlette), all for dried fruit in winter; grafts from friends' favourite fruit trees and a compost toilet.

Food should be grown locally wherever possible. Worldwide, livestock and humans place a heavy toll on water and fertile land; competition between such vital resources can lead to wars. I am a doctor by training and founded a registered charity, Solea Foundation, which integrates veganism within a holistic vision for ourselves and all life. This complements the activities of the Movement for Compassionate Living (the Vegan Way) which is currently working on details for Self-reliant, Tree-based, Autonomous, Vegan Villages (STAVVs). I hope my garden shows practical steps towards this vision.

64

Brickhurst Farm

After an indecisive start some 4 years ago whereby we fought with the National Planners to gain a temporary Agricultural Licence to apply permaculture design, this project is now firmly established, thanks to those who supported our bid to work with the land.

This 23.5 acre project has a greenwoods area which has been developed by dedicated and knowledgeable people and has many possibilities for future positive and integrated design and application. A small amount of raised beds are in experimental use and a community supported agriculture area is in existence. Water storage ponds have already been dug and we are in the process of developing a grey water system. The concept of Forest Gardening and Farming are in force with a wide biodiversity of useful plants and crops.

A Forestry Commission Woodlands Management Plan is being carried out and we hope to introduce old species that are vanishing due to legislation. There is much voluntary help needed in planning and practical hands-on work as we wish to instigate future projects, including: compost toilets, wind power and storage, traditional crafts and cottage industry and on to awareness healing, music and dance. Positive new energy is much needed for this exciting project to fulfil its potential and create an area of sustainability and self-sufficiency in which we can all share and enjoy.

Places can be allocated to applicants for up to a 6 month period with a mobile home and two benders on site and facilities for camping. We also offer regular 72 hour design and introductory courses for both rural and urban perspectives. For further information please send a SAE.

Address
Brickhurst Farm
Hastings Road
Pembury
TUNBRIDGE
WELLS
Kent
TN2 4BL

Telephone
(01892) 825697

Fax/E-mail

Contact
Danny

Date est.
1992

Size/acres
23.5

Residents
2

Visitors
BA

Goudhurst

Address
*c/o 15 Kemble
Drive
BROMLEY
Kent
BR2 8PY*

Telephone

Fax/E-mail

Contact
David Scott

Date est.
1993

Size/acres
21

Residents
None

Visitors
BA

I bought the 21 acre ex-hop garden in 1993. Prior to finding out about permaculture, my main inspiration had been the book, *Forest Farming* by J. Sholto Douglas and Robert Hart. Therefore the emphasis is very much on a productive woodland – tree cropping or Agroforestry. I was fortunate to meet Ben Law who is very much in tune with this. The larger part of the site was planted in the Winter of 1993/94 by Ben and myself. We also had the help of a number of volunteers on a couple of tree planting weekends.

Ben had obtained a grant from the Forestry Authority and this included a Better Land Supplement as it had previously been in agricultural production. He also obtained the Broadleafed Woodland Grant and even a grant for the design! The only restriction this caused was that we had to choose species acceptable to the Forestry Authority and plant at their recommended distances. Most woodlands planted today comprise two or three tree species – we planted twelve.

We planted an area of sweet chestnut coppice to be grown for hop poles, post and rail fencing and pales. The woodland edge was greatly extended with the use of 6-7 metre wide rides, which will be cut twice a year, encouraging wild flowers. Along these rides fruiting edge species were planted: crab apple, wild service, guelder rose, rowan and cherry.

Ten coppice blocks (5 hornbeam for firewood, 5 lime for green wood turning) were planted on corners of the rides. They are small blocks of around 80 trees for ease of management. Further away from the edge are the high value timber species of which oak makes up about 30%. The rest is made up of ash and wild cherry, with holly randomly planted to allow some evergreen cover with hazel producing a lower layer. Alder has planted throughout to fix nitrogen and can be coppiced like the woodland blocks near it.

The land is now clearly showing its own preferences and one of the two unplanted areas is now thickly stocked with self-sown trees. Black topsoil is also noticeably appearing in the same area. Having established the site, I am keen to make minimal intervention, with the farm essentially looking after itself.

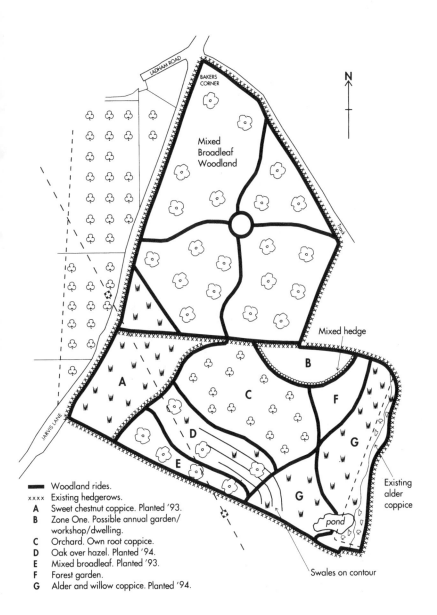

Woodland rides.
xxxx Existing hedgerows.
A   Sweet chestnut coppice. Planted '93.
B   Zone One. Possible annual garden/
    workshop/dwelling.
C   Orchard. Own root coppice.
D   Oak over hazel. Planted '94.
E   Mixed broadleaf. Planted '93.
F   Forest garden.
G   Alder and willow coppice. Planted '94.

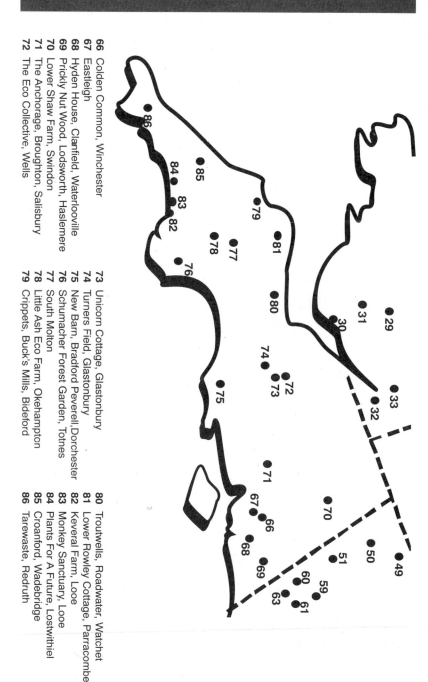

104

I moved here three years ago. The garden had the usual lawns, privet hedges and leylandii and also a stone paved yard. The first year the leylandii and privet hedge went and a dozen different apple trees were planted, which should produce over ten months of the year when they've grown a bit. My aims are:

- To become as self-sufficient in food as is practicable without spending too much time on it.

- To reduce non-renewable energy inputs.

- To conserve water as much as possible.

- To make it a really special place to be.

I want to create an integrated system which is practical, productive and looks good, which I can use to show people what permaculture is all about, as well as just talking about it. So far there are 30 fruit trees, including quince, medlar and fig, various sorts of soft fruit and quite a few herbs. The lawn is gradually turning into growing beds, mainly annual salad crops now, but gradually becoming more perennial as things are grown from seed. Heat for the house and the kettle is provided by coppiced and thinned trees from my work.

Future plans include arches and supports for more vertical planting, edible hedges and a greenhouse from old windows acquired through the local LETS, which is also a good source for old carpets for mulching. I'd also like to make use of solar and possibly wind energy – but that's for the future.

66

Colden Common

Address
52 Spring Lane
Colden Common
WINCHESTER
Hampshire
SO21 1SB

Telephone
(01962) 712440

Fax/E-mail

Contact
Ken Wilkinson

Date est.
1993

Size/acres
0.2

Residents
1

Visitors
BA

67

Eastleigh

Address
25 Chamberlayne Road
EASTLEIGH
Hampshire
SO50 5JN

Telephone
(01703) 613572

Fax/E-mail

Contact
Andy Waterman

Date est.
1990

Size/acres
0.2

Residents
2

Visitors
BA

I live in a mid-terrace house in town with a 17 x 5 metre back garden, here I keep two chickens, a rabbit, two wormbins and produce eggs, summer vegetables, salads, runner beans, silver beet (Swiss chard), several soft fruit, cucumbers, tomatoes and herbs. In winter I grow kale, leeks and parsnips, all under sown with white clover. These are my Zones 1 and 2 – and some experimental plants. See 'Backyard Bliss' in *Permaculture Magazine* no. 9.

When I moved in some years ago there was a massive population of very large black slugs. They have been jumped on, clobbered and generally massacred, very labour intensive and a dreadful waste of protein. Ducks could eat the slugs but they would have turned the garden into a quagmire and devastated my little wildlife pond, so I decided to try chickens. I bought two brown point of lay Rhode Island Red pullets. The chooks learned to eat grass so avidly that I never needed to mow the 'lawn' and when called, they would come to eat the slugs and woodlice from under the strategically laid pieces of carpet or wood. They run about on 20 sq.m. of grass, with a further 12 sq.m. of forage/soft fruit/ex-flower beds. This appears to be adequate although it can be a bit muddy in winter!

On my 10 rod allotment (Zone 3) I grow my main crops: potatoes, pumpkin, onions, garlic, broad beans, sweet corn, carrots, beetroot, brassicas, more leeks and parsnips plus experimental crops – kumara (sweet potato), millet, buckwheat and wheat. Three years ago I started to grow my own fertilisers/green manure and have designed a system that seems to be working very well, undersowing crops with white clover, alfalfa, lupins, vetches and rye, adding comfrey leaves (grown around the plot to keep couch grass at bay) and rotating crops on a five year basis.

The allotment is five minutes walk from home and being a no-dig system (except for the spuds!) is very little work, average one or two hours per week and I never need to buy vegetables. My fortnightly grocery bill is between £10 and £12, all other food is home grown. Visitors are welcome anytime and I can usually accommodate but please phone first to confirm.

Above: Zones 1 and 2 – intensive soft fruit and vegetables, chickens and a rabbit.

Below: Zone 3 – main crop vegetables.

68

Hyden House

Address
Hyden House
Little Hyden Lane
Clanfield
WATERLOOVILLE
Hampshire
PO8 0RU

Telephone
(01705) 596500

Fax/E-mail
(01795) 595834
permaculture@
gn.apc.org

Contact
Tim Harland

Date est.
1991

Size/acres
0.5

Residents
4

Visitors
BA

Hyden House is a family house and the home of *Permaculture Magazine*. The dwelling consists of two converted 19th century flint cottages set in half an acre of land on the edge of the South Downs. When we moved here in 1986, the back garden was the size of a pocket handkerchief. In 1991, we managed to acquire 0.3 acre of intensively farmed arable land adjoining the back garden. The garden plot is 65 x 20 metres, sloping gently east towards the house.

Our first move was to sow a wildflower mix (Cricklade SSSI mix) over the entire site for 'instant' diversity and to cover the eroded soil. Following this, we planted 700 mixed indigenous hedgerow trees, many of which are food bearing, to create an eventual windbreak and border the site.

Now established are the composting systems, mulched vegetable garden and the annual, spring and summer meadows. The spring meadow is placed nearest the house and cut to provide a children's play area through the summer months. Sixty fruit and nut bearing trees have also been planted on different root stocks to eventually create a multi-layered canopy. The area of trees on the north side of the plot will form the upper levels of a forest garden which we are gradually underplanting with the shrub and herb layers. On the west border, a number of fast growing trees have been planted to provide timber for firewood and enhance the windbreak. Several wood piles have also been introduced to provide increased habitat diversity and small ponds have been dug to encourage slug control by frogs. The area in the northwest corner has been left as a semi-wilderness.

We have built a ramp from the patio area up into the spring meadow with terraced beds for a 'minimalist' self-seeding salad garden. We now also have bees, ducks and a rotational (eventually full forage) chicken system.

The house itself is currently being ecologically retrofitted to include a passive solar growing area, food store, compost toilet, solar panels and a number of energy saving features.

We helped start the South East Hampshire LETScheme and are involved with the EarthWorks Trust in establishing a Centre for Sustainability nearby.

Hyden House

Prevailing
SW Wind

A House
B Food store
C Salads and tender plants
D Patio
E Chicken rearing pen
F Greenhouse
G Wood store
H Culinary herbs
I Self-seeding salad terraces
J Rotational chicken runs (1-4)
K Chicken house
L Wilderness
M Bees
N Forest garden
P Children's forest garden
   playhouse (with water butt)
Q Duck run
R Vegetable beds (1-4)
S Tool shed
T Compost heaps
U Spring wildflower meadow
V Turfed wildflower earth mound
W Summer wildflower meadow
X Annual wildflower meadow

Fruit or nut trees (at maturity)
numbered for ID

Mixed indigenous hedgerow

Water butts

Fencing

0   5   10   15
scale in metres

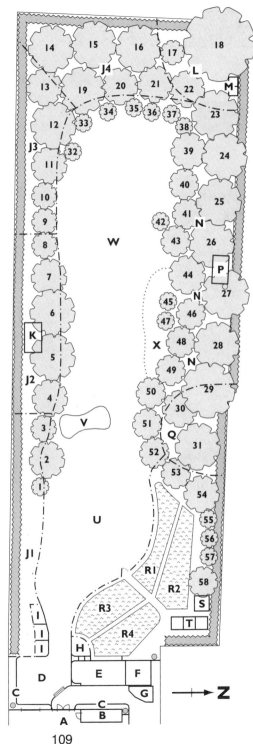

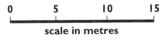

→ Z

69

Prickly Nut Wood

Address
c/o 69 Petworth Road
HASLEMERE
Surrey
GU27 3AX

Telephone
(01428) 656402

Fax/E-mail
(01798) 861406
Pager (0941)
100200 ex157133

Contact
Ben, Emma &
Rowan Law

Date est.
1992

Size/acres
8

Residents
3

Visitors
BA, WWOOF

In 1992 we acquired 8 acres of overgrown sweet chestnut coppice and rhododendron (by barter). The wood forms part of a larger area of coppice which is a Site of Special Scientific Interest for mosses, lichens and ferns. Initially we observed and learned who else was resident on the land before constructing our first bender and joining the delicate balance. Three benders later we continue to work the coppice integrating permaculture principles with the ancient patterns of the coppice worker as best we can.

The long term design is to cut most of the chestnut coppice on about a 12 year cycle, cutting about half an acre per annum; this allows enough light for good regeneration and gives a balanced succession of different aged coppice poles. It also always leaves at least one area freshly coppiced for our seasonal visitors – nightjars – who follow the coppice cycle.

A workshop for craft work and teaching blends in beautifully in a mossy glade. The walls are made from cord wood packed with clay from a pond we dug out (grant from Sussex Downs Conservation board) and the roof is turfed, on a self-supporting chestnut frame – design from the Hopi Indians.

Fruit trees have been planted to break up the coppice dominance and raised beds near the workshop look high on the agenda for 1996.

Our income comes primarily from charcoal production but we are planning a range of garden furniture for 1996. We are regenerating an area of mixed coppice: hazel, ash, rowan, oak and are constantly weaving brash hedges creating deer proof enclosures where needed.

We welcome this opportunity to learn directly from nature and look forward each day to the dawn.

Woodland workshop in Prickly Nut Wood, Lodsworth.

Lower Shaw Farm

Address
*Lower Shaw Farm
Old Shaw Lane
Shaw
SWINDON
SN5 9PJ*

Telephone
(01793) 771080

Fax/E-mail

Contact
*Frances Lewis,
Kevin Glaister*

Date est.
1974

Size/acres
3.2

Residents
4

Visitors
*BA, maintenance
weekends*

In 1974 Lower Shaw Farm was standing empty and unused and the outbuildings were barely fit for cows let alone humans. Since then the dairy and sheds have been converted to dormitories, meeting rooms and workshops and the garden worked organically. There are now two adults and two children living in the farmhouse; while the 'farm' itself is run as a meeting place for weekend and week-long courses. It has a steady stream of visitors throughout the year.

Lower Shaw Farm is now a three acre 'oasis' in an area of 1990s 'development'. Despite the loss of green fields, the farm has retained its character and atmosphere; and not far away is open countryside.

In January 1992 we hosted a workshop for permaculture design students wishing to gain practical experience. The result of this course was a comprehensive design – some of which we are now implementing stage by stage. So far, we have made a circle garden for bonfires, dancing etc.; planted fruit trees as the beginning of a forest garden; planted a fruiting hedge; and have a circular vegetable plot with mulched keyhole beds. We have also constructed a polytunnel and have built an 'eco' bathroom with compost toilets and a solar heated shower.

We have maintenance weekends when people can come and work in the farm doing gardening, painting and general maintenance in return for food and accommodation. We have a programme of weekend and week-long workshops which we will happily send on receipt of an SAE.

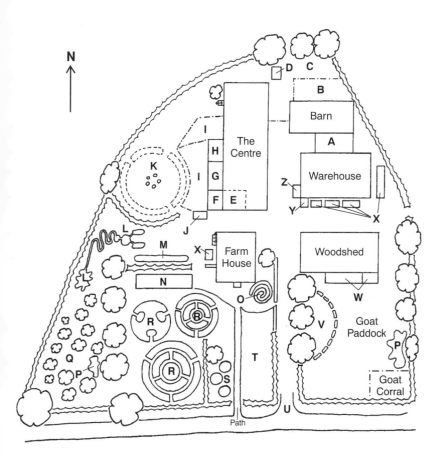

A	Covered yard	**N**	Polytunnel
B	Volleyball court	**O**	Herb spiral
C	Children's recreation area	**P**	Pond
D	Shed	**Q**	Forest garden
E	Eco-bathroom with compost toilet & solar heated water system	**R**	Vegetable plots
F	Milking shed	**S**	Children's vegetable plots with central ponds
G	Goat stalls	**T**	Wildflower meadow
H	Pony stable	**U**	Main entrance
I	Concrete livestock enclosure	**V**	Parking area
J	Shed	**W**	Chicken/greenhouse
K	The Henge – stones & fireplace	**X**	Caravans
L	Reed beds	**Y**	Coalshed
M	Compost heap	**Z**	Toolshed

71

The Anchorage

Address
The Anchorage
Salisbury Road
Broughton
STOCKBRIDGE
Hampshire
SO20 8BX

Telephone
(01794) 301234

Fax/E-mail

Contact
Julie & Steven Tidy

Date est.
1983

Size/acres
3.5

Residents
4

Visitors
BA, WWOOF

The Anchorage is a commercial organic holding producing vegetables and soft fruit to Soil Association standard, sold mainly through farm gate sales and more recently Community Supported Agriculture. We are situated on a north-facing hill top on shallow loam over chalk on the edge of Salisbury Plain. Because of this our main concerns are wind and water management.

After discovering permaculture in 1990, we began transforming our holding with a rolling programme of modifications and additions. This complements our efforts of the previous ten years, to develop methods of sustainable food production and living.

We believe that permaculture is of vital importance as a survival strategy, empowering people to regain some control over their lives and thus enabling action for change. Permaculture must be freely available to everybody. We are anxious to share experiences.

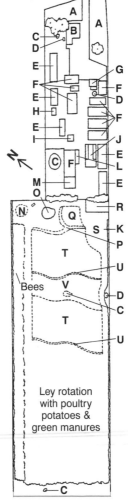

A   Fruit & nut plantings
B   Main house – long term energy efficient retrofit in progress
C   Pond
D   Water tank
E   Polytunnel
F   Shed/workshop
G   Roadside sales
H   Glasshouse
I   Demonstration urban garden
J   Chicken/greenhouse
K   Wind generator
L   Solar greenhouse
M   Energy efficient bothy
N   Experimental grey water treatment
O   Pit bender
P   Chalk banks
Q   Experimental lychet
R   Walled garden
S   Compost
T   Permanent vegetable beds with fruit
U   Temporary artichoke shelterbed
V   Orchard with nuts, soft fruit & herbs

Bees

Ley rotation with poultry potatoes & green manures

Above: Experimental lynchet.

Below: Conservatory for raising seedlings (and wine!) constructed from recycled materials.

72

Wells

Address
c/o The Eco Collective
33 North Road
WELLS
Somerset
BA5 2TL

Telephone
(01749) 620242

Fax/E-mail

Contact
Bob Moores

Date est.
1983

Size/acres
1.8

Residents
None

Visitors
BA

The Eco Collective is a network of committed grass roots professionals in the green/eco/ environmental movement, with experience going back 35 years. We see a beautifully simple, logically and empirically sound foundation upon which to base a new architecture, not one of style but one expressing and being itself within the whole environment; a much more gentle wholistic approach to creating our environment, which is its own inherent practicality. We believe that far from being an idealistic dream, this vision is not only a theoretical possibility but immediately realisable.

We can see a space where Nature is abundant and provides everything our physicality needs to stay healthy and strong, without any expenditure of effort or exploitation either of the earth or human beings. We are still on the same plot, which embodies the philosophy and practical details for people to see on the ground.

- We now keep bees.
- We are self-sufficient in carbohydrates, Vitamins A and C and proteins.
- Compost toilet at all stages of decomposition.
- Traditional high cider hedges with traditional integral coppices.
- Unique traditional South facing 10,000 year old terracing and aquifer control.
- Ditch to ditch soil conservation by traditional terracing and drought control methods.
- Nine traditional apple varieties amongst 80 trees, juicing and preserving techniques.
- Practical advice on planning permission, habitation, part-time residency etc..
- Wholeistic (holistic) personal practical guidance, by counsellors with over 30 years experience.

We are attempting to answer the logistical problems of locating human beings into Nature, to bring this culture into the here and now. We practice 100% Green Architecture – Live and Living Environments which provide shelter/food/air/water and clothing.

A half acre site developed from bare field site in 1985 and modified as a result of a permaculture design course since 1990. The site slopes gently to the northwest. Soil is heavy clay. A wide range of animal and plant species have been introduced with emphasis increasingly on low maintenance and perennial crops. A small income is derived from the sale of herb plants and craft items produced on site. Features include forest garden, poultry range, polytunnels, vegetable garden and tree nursery, orchards underplanted with comfrey; deep mulch beds are lined with woven willow boundaries which then strike as cuttings. Raised bed and keyhole configurations are used as well as more intensive systems in polytunnels and Zone 1. Shared ownership in woodland provides access to firewood and structural timbers. Geodesic dome and a modified caravan provide workshop and occasional sleeping space.

Further workshop/meeting space is also being added. Two ponds have been constructed at low points on the site boundaries and would make excellent collecting points for run off from polytunnels and tarmac areas.

The last year has been the proof of the pudding; we have fed ourselves and numerous visitors with very little effort.

The design has been developed over the past few years and is well stocked with plant species (more could be added). Further design work would focus on water conservation and the use of wind and solar energies. We have no animals at present but would like to have them again. Visitors are welcome by arrangement, especially those with ideas to share.

S & SW ENGLAND

73

Unicorn Cottage

Address
Unicorn Cottage
1 East Street
West Pennard
GLASTONBURY
Somerset
BA6 8NJ

Telephone
(01458) 833753

Fax/E-mail

Contact
Jo & Jonathan Fryer

Date est.
1985

Size/acres
0.5

Residents
4

Visitors
BA

74

Turners Field

Address
Turners Field
Permaculture
Compton Dundon
SOMERTON
Somerset
TA11 6PT

Telephone
(01458) 442192

Fax/E-mail

Contact
Ali Ingham,
Ann Morgan

Date est.
1986

Size/acres
3.6

Residents
3

Visitors
BA, WWOOF

Ann has been here for nine years and has planted many trees: fruit, nut and ornamental. We live in two connecting mobile homes and have a geodesic dome, hot tub and polytunnel. A wind generator provides electricity for lights and music; heat and hot water come from wood burning stoves. We use calor gas for cooking (plans for methane digestors are in discussion). We treat our own wastes with one of the few 'tree bogs' in the country. This is a dry aerobic composting system using untreated sawdust which feeds high biomass willows, growing at 3 to 4 times their normal rate.

The site is currently supplied with mains water, the waste going into soakaways. Plans include rainwater collection and purification, with plant systems for waste treatment. The recent building of two ponds, puddled traditionally with our own clay, are part of a planned comprehensive system. A reservoir will store drainage catchment and water will flow on down for irrigation, edible water plants, ducks, wildlife, then through reed beds into a clean water garden.

A design by Mike Keane including a larger windmill, passive solar collection, solar cells and inverter will become a demonstration for the promotion of green energy systems in the South West. Other plans include an edible forest garden, alongside a more traditional cider-apple orchard.

We have six chickens, three ducks, Hoppy the cat and Flo the dog. Our permaculture courses have been running for three years and we also run occasional more specific courses. We are adamant that true permaculture starts in Zone 00 and Zone 5 and continue to explore these issues as they come up. We work hard and celebrate the ordinary cycles of human life. We enjoy and often struggle with the ongoing exploration of ideas such as healing the generation and gender gaps and non-competitive communication.

Glastonbury is four miles away. You can reach us by bus or train to Castle Cary. Visitors can stay as WWOOFers or paying guests – please ring first. We are members of the HDRA seed group and will be open to the public this summer.

75

New Barn

Address
New Barn Field Centre
Bradford Peverell
DORCHESTER
Dorset
DT2 9SD

Telephone
(01305) 268865

Fax/E-mail

Contact
Neville Dear

Date est.
1989

Size/acres
20

Residents
Variable

Visitors
Anytime

Set amidst the rolling chalk downlands of Dorset in an area of outstanding natural beauty, the 18th century farmstead has been refurbished to provide accommodation, study and workshop facilities for groups of school children, together with a working pottery.

Over the past few years New Barn's twenty acres of farmland have been given back to nature for children to enjoy and study. Over one hundred million wild flower seeds went into the creation of traditional downland. A three acre hazel and ash coppice has been planted to provide fuel and fencing for the future. Traditional hedgerows with a wide range of species have been recreated. A wildlife pond and sanctuary for rescued amphibians and reptiles are popular with the children.

Whilst the whole centre is being developed along permaculture lines, a specific permaculture plot is developing well after three years:

- Forest garden, edible hedgerow and pond together with vegetable plot, raised beds and herb spiral are established.

- Our Earthship/Ecohouse is constructed of chalk filled scrap rubber tyres, old telegraph poles and living earth roof.

- Water borehole, wind and solar power are planned.

The permaculture plot demonstrates to visitors not only the principles of permaculture but also alternative technology and what life was like before we were farmers, i.e. when we were hunters/gatherers.

The reconstructed Iron Age homestead gives visitors a chance to see what life was like 2000 years ago. Essentially an educational resource for school children to use in 'living history' sessions, it also demonstrates a variety of earth building techniques. Walls of earth cob, daub and wattle and poles and roofs of wheat reed, heather, sedge, water reed and turf.

The aim is to transform a 2.1 acre field into a demonstration forest garden comprising many different levels of trees, shrubs and ground covers, all coexisting and producing fruits, nuts, medicinal products etc. It should be very largely self-sustaining, containing a very diverse number of species and thus very resilient to pests, diseases and the vagaries of the climate. It will be self-fertilising by the use of nitrogen fixing trees and shrubs (particularly Alders and *Elaeagnus*) and dynamic accumulators (e.g. comfrey).

The project will take some 10 years to plant out and a further 10 to reach semi-maturity. In the first year, propagation facilities were set up to grow most of the plants to be used on the site (a total of around 40,000 in 10 years).

In the first two years, trees and shrubs which form the 'backbone' of the forest garden have been planted. Grass is retained as the main ground cover, mown several times per year. Some 100 different species of tree and shrub crops will be used at this stage, from common species like apples, pears and plums, to less common ones like azaroles, chinkapins, cornelian cherries, highbush cranberries, honey locusts, Japanese pepper trees, medlars, mulberries, persimmons, quinces, strawberry trees and sweet chestnuts. An area of basketry willows has been planted in a wet area of the site.

Shrubs of varying sizes will occupy much of the space beneath trees, including common currants and berries and others such as barberries, *Elaeagnus*, Japanese bitter oranges, Oregon grapes, plum yews and serviceberries. Many of the understorey shrubs will be nitrogen fixers.

The grass ground cover will gradually be replaced over the 10 years with other ground cover species of use, most of which will have been propagated on the site. Some 3-4,000 plants per year will be planted out. Main species used for ground cover will include: Bamboos, especially dwarf species, carpeting species of *Rubus*, *Gaultheria* and Manzanitas, herbs and deep rooting perennials such as comfrey.

76

Schumacher Forest Garden

Address
Agroforestry Research Trust
46 Hunters Moon
Dartington
TOTNES
Devon
TQ9 6JT

Telephone

Fax/E-mail

Contact
Martin Crawford

Date est.
1994

Size/acres
2.1

Residents
None

Visitors
BA, open days
Jun & Sep

77

South Molton

Address
21 Churchill Crescent
SOUTH MOLTON
Devon
EX36 4EL

Telephone
(01769) 573272

Fax/E-mail

Contact
Susan Grime

Date est.
1991

Size/acres
0.016

Residents
2

Visitors
BA

There have been many changes made to this plot since the last edition. The paths have been removed because they were ugly and slugs liked to live down their sides. The whole garden is now a miniature forest garden containing soft fruits, herbs and wild salad crops, with a grass glade running down the middle. There is no longer an annual garden as such, although a few annual crops are dotted around the garden or grown in tubs on the patio, which keeps them away from the slugs.

The beech tree continues to grow slowly on the south side of the garden and although my boy is too big now for tree climbing, the conifer will stay because it links the garden with the sky. The herb spirals have gone. Stones are not a good idea in my garden, the slugs like them. The Mediterranean type herbs are grown on mounds or in tubs to keep their roots above the usually soggy conditions of the clay soil.

Rainwater levels are high. The clouds, being blown straight across the Atlantic, usually empty first on North Devon. Despite the dry conditions of summer 1995, none of my plants suffered permanent damage and the only watering necessary was the plants in tubs.

My new compost system consists of two plastic dustbins with their bottoms cut off. These are placed in holes dug to about one foot depth. Into these go kitchen wastes, human waste, wood ash and some garden waste. When the bins are moved on, the compost stays behind in the hole with a top dressing of twiggy garden waste. The herbs gradually grow over. I think it works, but it is early days yet. It certainly avoids heavy work and uses only a little ground at any one time.

In the house I am learning various processes to bring out the uses of produce grown in the garden. Examples are – preserves, wines, herbal teas, ointments, shampoo and washing solutions. I will probably sell these things through the local LETS.

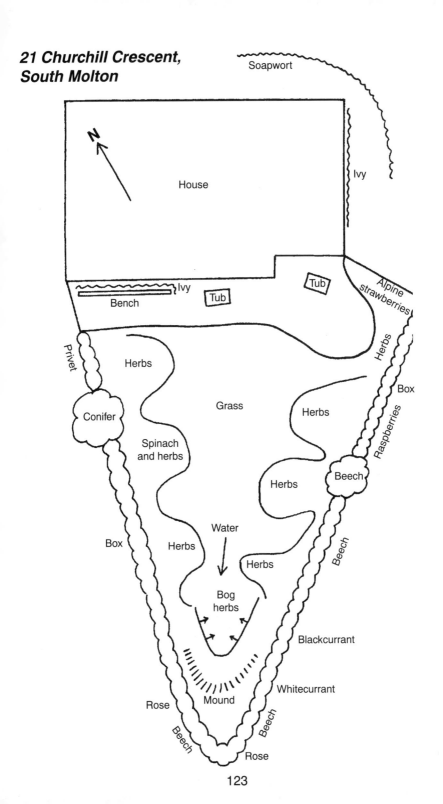

21 Churchill Crescent, South Molton

Soapwort

House

N

Ivy

Ivy

Bench

Tub

Tub

Alpine strawberries

Privet

Herbs

Herbs

Conifer

Grass

Herbs

Box

Spinach and herbs

Raspberries

Herbs

Beech

Box

Herbs

Water

Herbs

Beech

Bog herbs

Blackcurrant

Whitecurrant

Mound

Rose

Beech

Beech

Rose

78

Little Ash

Address
*Little Ash Eco Farm
Throwleigh
OKEHAMPTON
Devon
EX20 2HY*

Telephone
(01647) 231394

Fax/E-mail

Contact
*Marthe Kiley-
Worthington*

Date est.
1983

Size/acres
80

Residents
3

Visitors
BA, WWOOF

Little Ash Ecological Farm is 60 acres of grade 2/3 land and 20 hired acres. It has a 4 acre mixed deciduous woodland, 2 acres of field vegetables and fruit. It has two permanently running streams and a couple of ponds. 10 acres of arable cereal crops are grown annually (approximately 2 acres wheat, 3 oats, 5 barley and dredge corn, small area of trial maize 1989, linseed 1990, naked oats and triticale 1991) and rotated with the 60 acres or so of grass which is carefully managed. It is divided by double fences and establishing hedges into some 12 paddocks. The farm thus has a range of natural and managed habitats. It is run in conjunction with Little Druimghigha, a 70 acre eco-croft on the Isle of Mull, Argyll.

The objectives for the development of Little Ash are to develop it as a productive efficient farm with a sound financial basis, but also a farming practice that is sympathetic to the environment of the National Park and which in addition efficiently produces food and a living for the farmers without inputs to the system, increases rurally based employment and provide limited educational and recreational facilities without any environmental detriment. The whole farm is a conservation area. It is 'ultramodern' agriculture for the 21st century.

An ecological farm is defined as 'self-sustaining, diversified, high yielding, socially, ethically and aesthetically acceptable and causing no long term or irreversible environmental changes'. Airy fairy? No, we have demonstrated that this is possible on two previous farms, one in Sussex and one in the Hebrides over the last 20 years. At Little Ash we are not only developing and running an ecological farm, but also experimenting with ecological living for the farmers by reducing resources for housing, producing our own power etc..

T he permaculture plot at Crippets consists of a small 17th century stone and cob (mud) fishing cottage with 1/8 acre of land in the small hamlet of Buck's Mills on the North Devon coast. The plot faces south east and is situated on a plateau overlooking the hamlet at a point where the valley meets the sea and is surrounded by native woodland.

The various strategies in the garden include: mini forest garden (which has been adopted by the woodland and its wildlife), perennial and self-seeding annual vegetables, salad and fruit, several stone raised beds, herbs and various hedge species, fungi, and a small pond fed by rainwater is planned for the future.

As well as obtaining a high proportion of produce from our land and surrounding woodlands, we also harvest food and fertilisers from the sea. We are currently carrying out research into mariculture (shoreline permaculture) and hope to hold an introductory course in the future. We have a small boat and several lobster pots and are lucky to be able to stock up with all types of fish and crustacea for the winter months.

The building has been recently ecologically renovated including extensive structural repair due to subsidence. The opportunity to create a porch to shelter the front door was taken. A reused solid fuel Rayburn heats the house, hot water and is used for cooking – fuelled by wood from the adjacent woodland. Particularly efficient and attractive insulation (by night) and seat (by day) window Fabric-shutters cunningly designed and made by Maria help to keep us warm.

The strategies used include: increasing energy efficiency, use of renewable energies, use of materials from sustainable sources, use of organic materials that do not pollute in their manufacture or use and can be recycled, use of local materials and skills, rain and spring water collection.

The landscape and building work have been designed by Gale & Snowden, who provide a full permaculture design service in architecture, landscapes and interiors throughout the UK. They can be contacted at: 11A Litchdon Street, Barnstaple, Devon EX32 8ND. Tel. (01271) 326638.

79

Crippets

Address
Crippets
Buck's Mills
BIDEFORD
Devon
EX39 5DZ

Telephone
(01237) 431849

Fax/E-mail

Contact
David Gale,
Maria Stubbs

Date est.
1990

Size/acres
0.08

Residents
2

Visitors
BA

80

Troutwells

Address
Troutwells
Higher Hayne
Roadwater
WATCHET
Somerset
TA23 0RN

Telephone
(01984) 641330

Fax/E-mail

Contact
Rosemary &
Michael Littlewood

Date est.
1992

Size/acres
2

Residents
2

Visitors
BA, WWOOF

Troutwells is situated in a valley on the fringes of the Exmoor National Park. About half the site is on the hillside and the rest is on the valley bottom next to a small stream. We arrived in March 1992 and one of our first major tasks was to remove considerable numbers of conifers which covered the hillside and to thin out the alders 20-30 metres high on the steam bank. This gave us the light we so desperately needed to grow our edible crops, trees, shrubs etc..

The next major task was to create a network of paths in order to reach various locations and facilities. I have only just stopped borrowing in 'scalpings' (a local base course), over 100 tons in 4 years. It may seem extravagant but for pushing a loaded wheelbarrow up and down hills in wet weather it is essential.

After the removal of the conifers creeping buttercup took over and started to cover all but our young fruit trees. We dug this out by hand as we did not want to spray, which took quite a time. Afterwards we covered the ground with straw and whatever compost we could make. We estimate that we have used over 150 bales of straw, along with green manures.

Gradually we have managed to use all the hillside for fruit and nut trees, fruit bushes, herbs and plants for wildlife as well as companion planting. Around every tree we have planted garlic and nasturtiums with poached egg plant around all the currants, plums, damsons and gooseberries. In leftover spaces – pumpkins, gourds etc. The vegetables are grown on the flat land on slightly raised beds 1200-1500mm wide and 6m long surrounded by herbs, perennials, grasses and shrubs. At the northern end we have our mini-wood for fuel.

We have reshaped the stream banks as well as add rocks and boulders to the stream to create pools and waterfalls, which the very small trout appreciate. They return each spring and of course herons and kingfishers follow. We have tried and are still trying to combine good design with function and habitats for wildlife. From visitors comments we think we are on the way to creating a true Forest Garden in harmony in nature.

Troutwells 'Forest Garden'

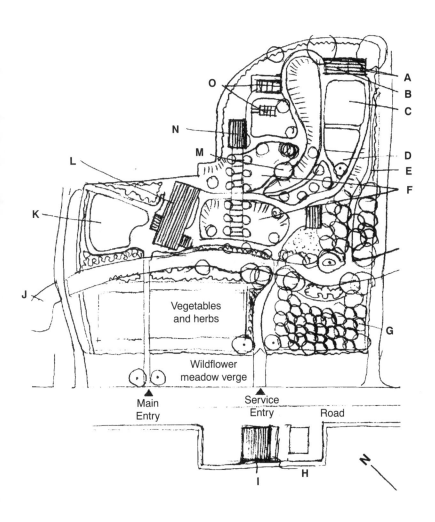

A	Wood shed	**H**	Store
B	Tool shed	**I**	Garage
C	Compost, leaves etc	**J**	Stream
D	Comfrey bed	**K**	Lawn
E	Minor stream	**L**	Cottage
F	Fruit and nut trees and bushes with ornamentals for wildlife on hillside	**M**	Look-out gazebo
		N	Office
G	Woodland for fuel	**O**	Greenhouses

Lower Rowley Cottage

Address
*Lower Rowley
Cottage
Parracombe
BARNSTAPLE
Devon
EX31 4PN*

Telephone
(01598) 763394

Fax/E-mail

Contact
Chris & Jewel

Date est.
1976

Size/acres
0.5

Residents
4

Visitors
BA

I n a clearing beside a spring in a once wooded valley on part of the moor in Southern England a house and barns were constructed using quarried stone, mud from the stream, oak from the forest and reed from the marshes. Many changes have taken place during it's and its' inhabitants evolution, bringing it back from its lengthy uninhabited derelict condition to its present residency of interested permaculturists.

The house here when purchased from its then owners (folk that had seen several generations under the same roof) had been abandoned; left for the cows to shelter in and somewhere to keep some winter feed. It was to be a lengthy project to develop the place into a Green Planet Base Play Station; somewhere that could provide education and retreat facilities which would include organic cultivation, low impact technology, animal husbandry, crafts, rural skills – permaculture etc.. Somewhere that the lifestyle was so close to the earth that it would be possible to observe and learn about first hand our human interaction and interplay with all the life forms that are around us.

We are hoping to expand our plot by a further four acres and be able to offer some small group camping space, with preference given to inner city groups, those interested in alternative technology and environmental artists.

Keveral Farm became an organic farm community in 1973 and comprises farmhouse, farm buildings and 25 acres of land. Extra dwelling space is provided by caravans, tipis and benders. The house is the focus of community life, with communal rooms, shared meals, social space and meeting space. There are 12-16 people living here and we have a Housing Co-op to run the house and a Workers' Co-op to run the farm.

We have four polytunnels, a walled garden and other outdoor growing areas and also keep goats and chickens. We have 8 acres of woodland, a young orchard and we are establishing new areas of woodland. We are working towards an integrated farm plan, including a more eco-friendly house. We are establishing a camping area for groups and individuals and also farm trails and educational facilities. We have a Visitor's Barn for courses, workshops and parties.

People come to Keveral for many different reasons, but most of us wish Keveral to become a more self-reliant and sustainable community, whilst also interacting with the wider community. We are involved in the local LETScheme and with Radical Routes, a self-help network of co-ops which uses ethical investment to give start-up loans to its member co-ops.

The community is in the process of buying Keveral and this should focus our minds on working more co-operatively and efficiently. We have also set up a new co-op – Keveral Sustainable Land Holdings – with the aim of buying more land in the local area, using loans from interested parties and then selling long term leases on plots of various sizes for sustainable development projects.

If you would like to find out more, or if you would like to visit and get involved with the community and communal work, then please write to the Visitor Co-ordinator, enclosing a SAE and saying a bit about yourself, why you would like to visit and when – and then wait patiently for a reply! If you would like to visit as a self-contained camper (£2 per night – we are just a short walk from the beach) then just phone us in advance.

82

Keveral Farm

Address
Keveral Farm
Seaton
LOOE
Cornwall
PL13 1PA

Telephone
(01503) 250215

Fax/E-mail

Contact
Oak, Eileen

Date est.
1972

Size/acres
30

Residents
12-16

Visitors
BA

83

Monkey Sanctuary

Address
Monkey Sanctuary
LOOE
Cornwall
PL13 1NZ

Telephone
(01503) 262532

Fax/E-mail

Contact
Kate or Paddy

Date est.
1992

Size/acres
12

Residents
8

Visitors
*BA, working
volunteers*

The Monkey Sanctuary was established in 1964 to provide a stimulating environment for woolly monkeys rescued from lives of isolation in zoos or as pets, and was the first place they bred successfully in captivity. Although woolly monkeys in the Amazon rainforests are threatened by habitat destruction and hunting, eventually it is hoped to return the colony to their native habitat and a charity has recently been formed with that objective in mind. The Monkey Sanctuary educates its many visitors and school groups about the need for conservation of the rainforest and native wildlife, for which most of its grounds are managed. Most of the workers, including volunteers, live on site as a community.

The Monkey Sanctuary has two permaculture areas in the grounds. A forest garden area was established about three years ago. It has started producing perennial semi-wild green leaves for the monkeys (and some of the tougher stomached members of staff), which provide a vitamin-rich and medicinally valuable supplement to their conventional salad diet. The area will also provide shoots, roots, nuts and fruits as the area becomes better established. Equally important it will hopefully show visitors some ideas on alternative gardening and less environmentally destructive ways of living. The other area consists of a large orchard which will provide fruit for the monkeys. This area is not open to visitors and is where we compost waste from monkey enclosures.

We would like the sanctuary to become a good example of living without exploiting the world's resources and creatures, in a way that is very accessible to summer visitors and tourists. We hope they might leave with inspiration, or at least get exposed to some ideas of slightly different ways of living.

The Monkey Sanctuary is open to the public April to October when the forest garden can be seen, but those wanting to see all the forest garden areas should do so by prior arrangement (Summer or Winter). Residential volunteers help care for the monkeys and in Summer work with visitors. Gardening, maintenance and construction work is done during the Winter. People with relevant skills particularly welcome.

Monkey Sanctuary Forest Garden

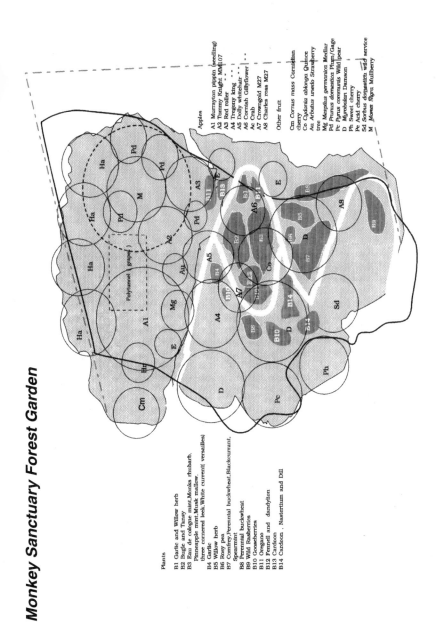

Plants

B1 Garlic and Willow herb
B2 Bugle and Tansy
B3 Eau de cologne mint,Monks rhubarb,
   Pineapple mint,Musk mallow,
   three cornered leek,White currant(versailles)
B4 Garlic
B5 Willow herb
B6 Rosy pea
B7 Comfrey,Perennial buckwheat,Blackcurrant,
   Spearmint
B8 Perennial buckwheat
B9 Wild Rasberries
B10 Gooseberries
B11 Oregano
B12 Fennel and   dandylion
B13 Cardoon
B14 Cardoon . Nasterticum and Dill

Apples

A1 Murrayton pippin (seedling)
A2 Tommy Knight MM107
A3 Red roller
A4 Tregony king
A5 Dolby whitehair
A6 Cornish Gillyflower
Ac Crab
A7 Crowngold M27
A8 Charles ross M27

Other fruit

Cm Cornus mass Cornelian
   cherry
Co Cydonia oblonga Quince
Au Arbutus unedo Strawberry
   tree
Mg Mespilus germanica Medlar
Pd Prunus domestica Plum/Gage
Pc Pyrus communis Wild pear
D Myrobolan Damson
Ph Sweet cherry
Pe Acid cherry
Sd Sorbus domestica wild service
M Morus Nigra Mullberry

131

84

Plants For A Future

Address
The Field
Higher Penpoll
St Veep
LOSTWITHIEL
Cornwall
PL22 0NG

Telephone

Fax/E-mail

Contact

Date est.
1990

Size/acres
28

Residents
Variable

Visitors
BA

Plants For A Future is a vegan alternative plant project that has started in Cornwall. Its aim is to demonstrate the wide variety of useful commodities such as food, fibres, medicines etc. that can be obtained from plants grown outdoors in temperate regions. We have 28 acres of south facing but exposed land. We have planted 12 acres of woodland and a mile or so of hedges as well as over 2 acres of beds containing a rapidly increasing variety of useful and unusual plants – at present about 1,500 species.

We are trying to build up a vegan community based around the plant project but at present we are unable to live on the land, living in houses and flats about 2 miles away. This community is aiming to become self-sufficient in food, fuel etc. as well as showing others that these can be derived from the plant world without recourse to animal exploitation or environmentally damaging methods. We feel that human survival depends on this and on the use of a wide variety of plant species, especially when there is a threat of rapid climatic change. Perennial plants are emphasised, because once these become established they require minimal disturbance to the soil, minimal environmental impact and minimal work.

We welcome visitors for day visits or occasionally longer stays. If our plans work out, from 1996 we will be open to the public on Sundays throughout April until September, so please visit then. If you do want to stay longer, please write. We are looking for new community members, but rarely have accommodation to offer.

We have a wide range of leaflets available on various aspects of plants and their uses. We also have a computer database containing information on over 6,800 species suited to temperate climates. We make this available on a donations basis and from 1996 we will be able to supply it in an easy-to-use format for those without their own database software. We also produce a catalogue, available for £1, of unusual and useful perennial plants which we can supply.

Above: Emily forages among the alpine strawberries.

Below: One of a number of ponds for pest control and growing edible and useful plants.

Wadebridge

Address
The Barn
Croanford
WADEBRIDGE
Cornwall
PL27 6JG

Telephone
(01208) 841660

Fax/E-mail

Contact
Trevor, Charlie &
Jacki Lawrence

Date est.
1993

Size/acres
7.5

Residents
3

Visitors
BA

Croanford is an old, unspoilt Cornish hamlet where we have a scattered smallholding on 7.5 acres of rather poor, hilly land. We are in North Cornwall, 3 miles from Wadebridge, 11 miles from the coast and adjacent to a mixture of intensively managed farmland and neighbouring woodland.

The smallholding consists of about 1.5 acres of home garden, forest garden and paddock, with the remaining land about half a mile distant in two directions. This is mainly pasture but includes one acre of ancient, neglected coppice, predominantly hazel and ash.

Within the home garden area is a 60 x 20 foot Dutch-light greenhouse at present in the early stages of establishment. Next to the greenhouse is a fairly level vegetable plot for mainly annual crops and the bank behind (approximately 0.3 acre) is fenced for chickens and fruiting tree and shrub planting has been commenced. This area has only recently become available and part is still a jungle of hazel, elder and very invasive wild clematis. It is gradually being cleared with the aid of the chickens. Adjacent paddock is bordered by a stream.

Separated from the property by a lane is a further forest garden of longer establishment, with apples (some rare), pears, plums, damsons, soft fruit and a wide range of other edible perennials. There is a service area with sheds, compost bins and propagating beds for cuttings and young trees. Some annual crops are interspersed with the perennials and a good range of pick and pluck salad plants and herbs.

Livestock kept on the holding include Rhode Island Red and Black Rock hens, Brecon Buff geese, Dexter cattle, bees, cat and dog. Some produce is sold but most is for our own consumption.

We came here in January 1992, inspired by a visit to Robert Hart and a permaculture weekend. We have a small garden facing southeast and a field which slopes to the southwest. Apart from a small stand of pines in the western corner, the field was all grass with a series of small strip beds. We found these were soon swamped by couch grass and we reduced the edge by joining them together with the barrier-mulch method. This provided an ideal environment for slugs and we had no crops! However, the resulting soil was much improved and full of worms. A pond for frogs and toads has now brought slugs under control. We found that the cardboard barrier doesn't kill couch grass; the roots build up a dense mat beneath it and sprout up when the cardboard has decayed, soon smothering seeds.

We are establishing an area of forest garden with apple and cherry trees, soft fruit and an understorey of herbs, which I dry for teas. The ground was not cleared but repeatedly mulched with organic straw from old thatch.

A network of hedges provide shelter. The early ones were quick and cheap: *Escallonia* and flowering currant. We are now planting fruiting hedges: *Rosa rugosa*, *Elaeagnus*, *Berberis darwinii*, sea buckthorn. We're also trying out many unusual fruits from Plants for a Future. I recommend their catalogue.

We still have a vegetable plot for conventional annuals. We tried polyculture broadcasting, without success. We are now using Gertrud Franck's methods (from her book, *Companion Planting*). We eat something from the plot for most months of the year. In the drought we pumped out the septic tank onto part of the vegetable plot.

Beehives have increased fruit crops. We have used some of the pines for firewood and acorns are germinating in their place. We have planted many native trees; wildlife includes foxes, frogs, toads, bats and an increase in birds. We've had few visitors but the local horticultural college are bringing students.

86

Redruth

Address
The Cottage
Tarewaste
REDRUTH
Cornwall
TR15 3SJ

Telephone
(01209) 212738

Fax/E-mail

Contact
Jo Pacsoo,
Frank Cooper

Date est.
1992

Size/acres
1

Residents
2

Visitors
BA

City
Farms

M any City Farms and Community Gardens have been following permaculture principles for years, some without realising it. Our method of agriculture is socially, environmentally and ecologically sound. People, plants, animals and the land become interdependent. We adopt conservation principles; we recycle many different materials and we design our projects to be as diverse as possible.

City Farms and Community Gardens are not conventional food-producing enterprises where the growing of crops and the raising of livestock is an end in itself. They are community projects. They create a stimulating environment and offer people opportunities that they would not experience otherwise. Some Farm and Garden projects have been going for over 20 years. People in several local communities set them up on derelict or under-used land in the inner city, on the urban fringe, or in new towns. There are now over 60 Farms at various stages of development and there are examples in most major cities in Britain.

These projects offer everyone a place to grow things and tend animals – it allows them to experience a wide range of rural activities and help manage the project on behalf of the community. City Farming is, therefore, of a peculiar nature, offering social welfare, employment, environmental, recreational and educational opportunities, as well as economic ones. Organic principles are usually followed because the people attracted to City Farming and Gardening are 'conservation conscious', and because in our situation ecological actions do work and are seen as necessary if sites are to thrive.

City Farms are faced with the same problems as other producers, but have other pressures too. On many, the soil is thin or stony, contaminated by various chemical or physical wastes.

Some sites are steeply sloping, poorly drained or infertile. Most are small in size, the average being 4.1 acres (0.5 to 90 acres). This small acreage has many demands placed upon it – pastures for livestock; cropping ground; areas for wildlife or educational work; play space; composting and recycling areas, to name but a few.

Address
National Federation of City Farms
The GreenHouse
Hereford Street
Bedminster
BRISTOL
BS3 4NA

Telephone
(0117) 923 1800

Fax/E-mail
(0117) 923 1900
102404.14@
compuserve.com

Contact
Chris Lillington

Then there are the human problems involved in managing a complex enterprise that co-ordinates core staff, volunteers, temporary employment and training schemes and a variety of placements. We have had to find ways of overcoming these limitations to make work easier and the projects succeed.

By adopting the principles of sustainable agriculture we have found that some tasks are easier to perform, the environment is improved, costs are reduced and productive cropping achieved on previously derelict sites.

Our husbandry aims are to:

- **Promote welfare** of people, animals and the environment, especially the land.
- **Be self-sustaining**, replenishing the soil, keeping insect numbers in balance through natural control.
- **Recycle resources** by composting, feeding discarded wastes to animals and salvaging timber.
- **Plan intensively** to produce as much from the land as possible.
- **Encourage diversity** by keeping a wide range of animals, growing a large collection of plants and developing diverse micro-climates by contouring, using windbreaks etc..
- **Integrate techniques** by bringing different disciplines together, such as ecology and architecture, introducing stock into gardens etc..
- **Save energy** by using appropriate technology, zoning the site, using natural fertilisers.

Permaculture is actively promoted by the National Federation of City Farms (NFCF). It began formally in 1984, when we arranged courses by Bill Mollison and Sego Jackson. These gave inspiration and helped us to structure the various ideas that had been evolving.

As a result of these courses, permaculture is covered in NFCF technical literature and periodicals. The principles are often central to the feasibility studies we conduct for new groups and established projects. In addition, permaculture applications are covered in training workshops that are run regularly throughout the country and in community gardening courses.

Some examples of City Farming practices include:

- Collecting roof water run off for watering in greenhouses.
- Animal shelters set into banks or grassed on their sides and roofs.
- Spiral herb gardens to cultivate both shade and sun loving plants in a limited space.
- Growing potatoes in stacks of old tyres for demonstration of patio/balcony growing techniques.
- 'Chicken tractor' giving poultry access to small runs radiating from central housing, with rotation of cropping.

The NFCF itself has a new timber office, demonstration and conference centre in Bristol, built in 1995, which incorporates a number of permaculture ideas and is completely covered with a grass roof. The building can be hired.

Difficulties Putting Permaculture into Practice

The time factor: When people come up with an idea for a City Farm, there is a great deal of initial enthusiasm. The legal aspects, fund-raising and project organisation can take a long time – perhaps 18 months or 2 years. By the time the land is made available, people's enthusiasm may have been dampened, so activities that yield a quick success are important.

Attitudes: It's true that people will do what they know best. Radical approaches will not be accepted unless the case is expertly sold and adequate back-up support is available. Unfortunately, there are few people with permaculture expertise in this country in the right places, who can support a voluntary group regularly over a long period.

Priorities: Projects are always short of money and this affects working practices and priorities. Everything else seems to take precedence over site landscaping because needs are more immediate.

Survival: Projects are under pressure in many areas as local authorities review their land stocks. A few sites are threatened with development. For some projects, day-to-day concern is with immediate survival, rather than with establishing a long term agro-ecosystem.

The City Farm Sites

A City Farm is a highly complex development. It will consist of many separate components, all of which have to be integrated successfully. Each site can have more than a dozen uses. On a very small area of land, as most projects are, many of the demands might conflict:

- Recreational activities.
- Educational schemes.
- Nature projects.
- Livestock husbandry.
- Fodder production.
- Children's pursuits (play/learning).
- Individual's needs (sanctuary/therapy).
- Social events (open days, fairs).
- Business operations (shop, café, market garden).
- Community festivals.
- Environmental improvement (landscaping, forestry).
- Gardening.

To make the most of available land, we follow these tenets:

- Use what you've got – turn a disadvantage into an advantage.
- Design elements to have many functions – if you can't find five uses for doing something, should you really be doing it?

As an example of the former, rather than draining a marshy hollow and turning it into pasture, we might use the area for wildlife, grow rushes for animal bedding, or produce aquatic plants as fertiliser and fodder.

Where possible, each element is given many different functions – over 18 for a hedge, for example. Similarly, site landscaping materials can also be used for animal fodder, pollen and nectar sources for bees, amenity, wildlife sanctuary and biomass for composting.

A field can be used as a pasture for animals to graze, exercise and be displayed and as recreational space. If sown with wild herbs the field can then become an attractive picnic area and the herbs will be eaten as medicines and tonics on-the-hoof. It could also be developed as a wild flower conservation meadow. With careful management, this one paddock can be developed to possess more than five functions and the value of that land to the project is increased many fold.

The Future

Many City Farms have the potential to develop as community businesses. Already set up are market gardens, cafés, shops and business starter units. In each case, income from these enterprises is returned to the neighbourhood City Farm project to support its social welfare and educational roles.

Also being considered is the use of Farms as neighbourhood distribution networks. A City Farm could link with a rural organic smallholder who would grow a range of products under contract. This food would then be made available to nearby households, which might participate in the scheme on a co-operative basis.

*Plant a Seed
and Grow
a Community*

National Federation of
City Farms

Plotting The Next Edition!

You are invited to submit your entry for the 1996/7 edition of *The Permaculture Plot*.

Please follow the existing style to include:

- Address and telephone number.
- Contact name.
- Date site/project established.
- Size (acres).
- Number of permanent residents.
- How people can visit:
  – welcome at all times;
  – welcome by arrangement;
  – through the WWOOF scheme (details on request);
  – cannot be accommodated;
  – no visitors, thanks.
- 300 words to describe your project.
- Plan of site – To include A4 size base plan **without** any text/key + a further A4 size copy of the same plan **with** text/key.
- Other photographs or illustrations that could be considered for including.

Please send your entry to Simon Pratt (*see address below*).

Simon Pratt
Compiler
July 1996

Editorial Address
Redfield Community Buckingham Road Winslow BUCKINGHAM MK18 3LZ

Telephone
(01296) 712161

Fax
(01296) 714983

E-mail
106031,2416@ compuserve.com
or
pcbritain@ gn.apc.org

Permaculture Association (Britain)

The Permaculture Association (Britain) is a registered charity (registration no. 290897) that acts as a vehicle for connecting people, ideas, resources and projects in Britain and throughout the world. As well as holding a conference and convergence once a year, its main function is to keep people in touch with one another and facilitate the spreading of information. Membership of the Permaculture Association gives you access to the following:

- Quarterly newsletter giving the latest permaculture network news.

- Local group contacts.

- International contacts.

- Courses – Permaculture courses are held regularly in various parts of Britain:

  Introductory Course – Usually a single weekend. Contains both information and practical work.

  Full Design Course – Comprising 72 hours' teaching. It is the foundation course for those wishing to take up permaculture design work, or implement permaculture in their own homes or on their own land. It is also for those in related professions who wish to add the permacultural perspective to their existing skills. Completion of the design course plus two years' work in permaculture, full or part-time, can lead to the qualification of Diploma in Permaculture Design (Dip. Perm. Des.).

  Specialist Courses – Covering specific subjects in detail.

  Details of current courses are available from the Permaculture Association as well as in *Permaculture Magazine*.

- Permaculture designers – A list of qualified designers is available on request, together with advice on how to choose the one who is right for you and your job.

Address
The Permaculture Association (Britain)
PO Box 1
Buckfastleigh
Devon
TQ11 0LH

Telephone
(01654) 712188

E-mail
pcbritain@
gn.apc.org

PUBLICATIONS
Turning Problems into Solutions...

Permanent Publications

PERMACULTURE MAGAZINE

Permaculture Magazine links you to a national and international network of like-minded individuals and organisations. Its contributors share with you their many years' experience of putting permaculture into practice – in diverse situations, settings and locations.

Packed with informative articles, designs, news, book reviews, letters, course information, contacts and permaculture groups near you – this unique magazine will inspire and inform **anyone who cares** about our environment.

Permaculture Magazine is published quarterly and contains 52 pages packed with photographs and illustrations.

Topics featured include:

Getting Started • Permaculture Gardening
Urban Permaculture • Forest Gardening • LETS
Ecological Housing • Community Gardening
Community Supported Agriculture
Alternative Technology • Network Listings

Price per 4 issues:
U.K.: £10.00. Europe: £12.00. Rest of World: £16.00 (Europe and Rest of World prices include Airmail p&p.)

FREE SAMPLE COPY: Send £1.00 (coin or stamps) to cover p&p costs.

PERMACULTURE IN A NUTSHELL
by Patrick Whitefield
With a preface by Jonathon Porritt

This inspiring book is a concise and accessible introduction to the principles and practice of permaculture in temperate climates.

It explains how it works in the city, the country and on the farm. It also explores ways in which people can work in co-operation to recreate real communities.

Address
*Permanent Publications
Hyden House Ltd
Little Hyden Lane
Clanfield
Hampshire
PO8 0RU*

England

Telephone
(01705) 596500

Fax
(01705) 595834

E-mail
permaculture@ gn.apc.org

Permaculture in a Nutshell clearly describes how we can live fruitfully and sustainably without plundering the Earth, and is essential reading for everyone wishing to find creative solutions for reducing their environmental impact.

Paperback; 96pp; 198 x 127mm; ISBN 1 85623 003 1

Price inc. p&p:
U.K.: £5.00.
Europe: £5.50 (Airmail).
Rest of World £5.50 (Surface). £6.50 (Airmail).

HOW TO MAKE A FOREST GARDEN
by Patrick Whitefield
With a foreword by Robert A. de J. Hart

A step-by-step, DIY guide to creating a maximum output food producing garden for minimum labour, based on the ecological model of a natural woodland. This highly practical, yet inspiring book gives you everything you need to know in order to create a beautiful and productive forest garden, including:

Basic principles • Layout • How to choose plants
Detailing over 100 plants, from apples to mushrooms.
A comprehensive account of perennial and
self-seeding vegetables.
A step-by-step guide to creating your garden.
Full details of an example garden,
and pictures of many more.

Forest gardening is an important element of permaculture and this book explains permaculture design for temperate climates in detail.

Paperback; 192pp; 275 x 210mm; 10 colour and 35 b/w photos + 65 line drawings. ISBN 1 85623 008 2.

Price inc. p&p:
U.K.: £17.00.
Europe: £19.50 (Airmail).
Rest of World £19.50 (Surface). £23.00 (Airmail).